DIGGING DEEPER WITH THE DUCHESS

DIGGING
DEEPER
with the
DUCHESS

Sam Llewellyn

Published by
New Hat, an imprint of
The Marine Quarterly Ltd
The Hope, Lyonshall
Kington
Herefordshire HR5 3HT UK

Telephone +44 (0)1544 340636
editor@marinequarterly.com
www.diggingwiththeduchess.co.uk

ISBN 978-0-9927688-6-7

Front cover image by Simon Dorrell

Typeset in Van Dijck at Five Seasons Press
Hereford UK
www.fiveseasonspress.com

Printed by Graficascems, Polígono Industrial
San Miguel 31132 A (Navarra) Spain

CONTENTS

Preface

A few years ago, quarterly essays about the garden at the Hope began appearing in *Hortus*, the world's most beautiful (and least illustrated) gardening journal. When the *Hortus* essays began, they were strictly about the practicalities of a large and wild garden in the Welsh Marches. Then one summer morning I found a Duchess slumped against the sculpture known as the Giant's Keyring on the West Lawn. Judging by the amount of dew on her she had been there all night. I helped her into a hot bath, gave her lodging in the Tower, and bent an ear to her speech, which was rapid and toxic.

She turned out to be a keen gardener, who had experienced more than the adult dose of sex and death, which is after all the main business of gardens, beauty being a by-product. She had sublimated her experience of these into a fierce urge for Plymouth gin and Capstan Full Strength cigarettes, from which over the next few years she allowed herself to be partially weaned; though in our travels and horticultural experiments any idea that does not have her full approval still sends her straight back to the palliatives. Gardens, and indeed life itself, have therefore become a constant negotiation between her taste (appalling) and her craving for oblivion (also appalling, with sea shanties).

The essays in this book range over the garden at the Hope and beyond, and outline the compromises that must be made to maintain on the one hand the lawns, beds, woods and hedges, and on the other a relationship whose breakdown would make atomic fission look like an exploding gorse pod. I hope they will be of some use to people faced with large gardens, or indeed difficult relationships. So does she, or anyway she says she does, but I suspect she doesn't really give a monkey's. Ah, well.

Sam Llewellyn
The Hope
2020

Urbs in Rure

WE SPENT THE SPRING IN MALLORCA, the Duchess and I, so while Britain weltered in floods we were stumping up mule paths among trees jewelled with oranges and through olive groves gnarled and antique, bathed in grey-green sunlight. We ate *pan amb oli*, bread smeared with oil, salt, garlic and half-dried tomatoes, and looked out from cypress-spiked terraces at rafts of shearwaters on a sea made of sapphires. It was the simple life, made simpler by the fact that the Duchess managed to stay off the sauce. We returned to the Welsh Marches in time for everything to start growing. Daffodils flowered and went over at the foot of the *Metasequoia glyptostroboides* in the Caledonian Glade. Tulips followed on, and the borders swelled and burst, and maintenance set in.

So there I was in the middle of the croquet lawn removing crumbs of worm cast with a pair of surgical tweezers when I heard a whiz and a thud. And there, half embedded in the sward by my side, was a book – *Cold Cream* by Ferdinand Mount, to be precise: an interesting memoir of that great man's life, interspersed with moments of supreme hilarity.

I confess that at this point I was indignant on two counts, and worried on one. The croquet lawn is a moderately sacred spot, particularly when it has got Rural Deans competing on it (only the High Church ones seem to play, since they are able to get rid of the toxic levels of sin inherent in the game by Confessing each other in the aftermath). It is not a rubbish dump for discarded memoirs. Furthermore I had been hoping to read the book, and this was not going to be pleasant with large parts of it coated in a mixture of loam and lawn sand. Hence the indignation, and under normal circumstances I would have expressed it in the manner of a bucko mate in a typhoon. But it was tempered, as I say, by worry. I had a suspicion where the book had come from, and a glance upwards confirmed it. High above, the diamond panes of the drawing-room window in the West Tower glittered in the sun, and from within came the sound of a low, tense hissing. The bookflinger had been the Duchess, and with her what starts with bookflinging will if not headed off at the pass end in tears of pure gin.

I picked up the book and dusted it off. Scent was rolling down on me from the Zephirine Drouhin on the wall. The yews were dusted gold with new growth, the echiums were loud with bees, and on the roof of the Giant Egg a couple of swallows were gossiping in a long, pure, adulterous babble. What, I thought with a sinking of the heart, now?

The hissing in the tower was forming words. The Duchess seemed to be saying she was sick of something. Of what, though? As if she had heard my thought, she began to shout. She damned all bees, all birds, the Kiftsgate that was trying to grow in at her window, the newts in the pond by name, the ruddy sheep going baa, the ruddy cattle going moo, the ruddy sunrise and the ruddy stars. She was sick (she said, returning to her original theme) of living like a ruddy peasant in the middle of the ruddy country.

So let us go abroad again, I said; well, shouted.

But apparently she was sick of abroad too, because we always went to more country, only hotter, and anyway we had only just got back and what was I trying to do, turn her into a ruddy foreigner? She missed the smell of the traffic and the chance of running into clever people like Ferdy Mount. When, she said, was the last time we had been to a decent sort of town, like for instance, London or New York or Beijing?

Well of course the answer was about six weeks ago, and she had come home by Air Ambulance singing the Marseillaise in what she imagined was Mandarin. Fearing a relapse, though, I made soothing noises. A city break was not currently convenient, I said, given the aspect of the constellations, not to mention the tail end of the as-paragus, the artichokes and the peas (to name but a few) that were coming up like gangbusters in the kitchen garden. Perhaps in a month or two –

Another book hurtled out of the window, followed by a tea tray, a doubtful Matisse and a set of Peonies of China table mats in a presentation box. There was no sense in answering, and anyway I was getting a sore throat. I excavated the missiles from the turf, thinking the while, then went inside and made a telephone call to

Big Irma, late of the Colony Club, rehab veteran and exile from Soho, who popped over on her moped and talked metropolitan to the Duchess while I made feverish plans.

The next morning after breakfast I led the Duchess into what had been the Swamp Patio, a dankish place at the best of times, made even more villainous today by the fact that I had carpeted it with black aeoniums, to simulate tarmac, and had left a boombox in an adjoining shed hammering out ragga, to simulate neighbours. The sun was shining into the SP, as it does for half an hour every morning. We sipped city-grade cappucino from the Gaggia machine, while over the wall there floated the fumes of a bonfire made of old Ford Sierra tyres and waste oil to simulate the Great West Road. All the while I made brittle conversation about the Chelsea Flower Show, which I know the Duchess despises. A swallow whipped overhead and ate a butterfly.

'What was that?' the Duchess cried.

'An immigrant,' I said.

She frowned, wondering whether she should say something ought to be done. It was all going frightfully well.

She ate another couple of croissants and polished off her coffee. The sun had left the Swamp Patio, as it does many city breakfast spots. 'What,' I said, 'about a stroll in the park before we go shopping?'

We strolled. We passed between a couple of beds of hastily-planted begonias hand-scattered with fast food containers. I pointed out a new *Clematis orientalis*, which come autumn would be releasing into the air its trademark smell of hot steel, and some hastily plunged cyclamens of the wild variety, which always strike me as having a bracingly metallic niff. I then went and started the tractor, which provided a charmingly urban continuo for the songs of the thrushes, and asked if she was ready for shopping.

She frowned, and said she had letters to write, and went off and wrote them, having made a date for lunch. We met for a swift apple juice, then went in to the dining room, where Vladimir Scrounja, who runs a charming foraged-chic restaurant just off the King's Road, came in with a couple of plates covered with silver domes. He whipped off the cupolas, revealing his signature *tartare d'escargots aux fraises des bois aux laitues mimachées au jus de rampions* — a dish so recherché as to be inedible by anyone but a hedge fund manager's doxy, but urban, urban to an appalling degree. I noticed that the Duchess pushed it round the plate a bit, and made a remark about the charms of domesticated vegetables, as grown in the kitchen garden. I found myself crossing my fingers under the table.

After luncheon I took her to the cinema, which is to say sat on the sofa with her and watched an absolutely revolting film called the *Wolf of Wall Street*. She lasted five minutes, then said she was going to get a breath of air. I stayed on to look at some of the more interesting parts of the film, which is sound on salesmanship and orgies if nothing else, then went to look for her.

Scrounja had departed in a huff, and the kitchen showed signs of having been ransacked for bread, tomatoes, garlic and olive oil. I could not find her on the terrace, where we were scheduled to have tea delivered by Brown's Hotel. She was absent from the aeonium tarmac and the carpet bedding. I finally found her lying flat on her face in a little border.

For a moment my blood frankly curdled. It had all been too much for her, and she was back on the gin, and all was lost. I ran towards her, hauling the telephone from the pocket and stiffening the finger to dial the men in white coats. Then I realised that she was speaking. It was not the usual bad-tempered hiss, but a sort of crooning. Next to her nose was a toad lily. She was talking to it admiringly. It was one of those rare occasions when it was possible to see her point. Her aristocratic face was dusted with crumbs and slightly shiny with the oil of nourishing peasant foodstuffs.

My spirits began to lift. If she was eating *pan amb oli* and discussing the meaning of life with toad lilies, it seemed probable that her urban yearnings had left her. I cancelled Brown's Hotel, brewed strong tea and took her a pint mug, which she drank, wiping her mouth with the back of her hand. Then we restored the garden to its rural innocence. Until the next time it happens.

Politics

WHEREVER YOU LOOK, the Duchess was saying the other day, there seems to be politics. At the time I was attempting to chainsaw up a wych elm that had been blown down across a bunch of rhododendrons, and the task was proving as knotty as the grain, so this was not a welcome observation. But the Duchess has never cared much about welcomeness. So I stopped the saw, squeegeed the persp from the brow with the side of the hand and asked her what on earth she was on about.

'Politics,' she said. 'You are buried here in your rural fastness. The cries of the great world are drowned out by the death-rattle of aspirations.'

My scalp, I tell you, prickled, and the hairs of the head vibrated like quills upon the fretful porpentine. There I stood, flesh creeping. And I knew that I was in the same old spot. I had to get involved, because if I didn't it would be back to the bad old days, clouds of Capstan smoke and the knell-like clink of bottle on glass.

'The death of aspiration,' I said with as much hauteur as I could muster, having just tripped over a branch, 'is otherwise a kind of Zen calm.'

'What?' she said.

I turned off the chainsaw and tried again. She snorted. 'We stand,' she said, 'on the brink of a precipice.'

I nodded. Things were narrowing down. We were about to talk about the Scotland Referendum. And you could see what she meant. The idea of being sundered from some of my favourite cousins by a weird little demagogue with black eyebrows and about forty chins is disheartening. As for the Duchess, her forebears were in jute, or perhaps whisky, or it might have been basic slag. But her heart, as she often says, is in the highlands, a-chasing the beer, or perhaps she means deer, and if she has to hang around in the Scots Consulate queuing for a visa to visit her vital organs where does that leave her? It is a rhetorical question, of course, but unlike most such questions it has an answer, viz. face down in the shrubbery singing folk songs to the ants.

So I addressed myself to politics, without, of course, straying beyond the lodges that shield the Hope from the baneful influence of the outside world. The first thing to do was to stop the Duchess rushing up to Scotland to campaign, or we would never see the Long Border at Crathes Castle again, and the same went for the walled garden at Atholl Castle, the *Davidia involucrata* at Arduaine, and the Great Northern divers that cruise the loch in front of Osgood Mackenzie's wrought-iron sea gates at Inverewe.

The Duchess was resistant, but I prevailed. She stumped off to her rooms in the Tower, and came down a couple of days later with a sheaf of papers in her hand. In a low, tense voice she told me that her forebears had fought at Agincourt and abolished slavery in South Kensington, and that she needed to Get Involved. Next year, she said, was a general election, in case I hadn't noticed. She had designed some planting schemes to reflect this fact.

Smiling politely, I took the papers from her hand and sent her to stay with some cousins in the Languedoc, where they were having a non-alcoholic vendange of an entirely suitable nature. I then scrutinised her proposed plantings.

She seemed to have been channeling the Symbolic Carpet Bedders of the Victorian age: those brave gardeners who brought us the Children of Israel in begonias, wending their way through a wilderness of antirrhinums to a Promised Land of Dahlias Cactus Mixed via some miracles expressed in ferns, cycads and paving slabs ripped from the hovels of the tenantry. In the notes she had scrawled on her drawings (green ink, apparently using both hands) she had acknowledged her debt to these giants, but claimed to be approaching her plantings from a conceptual, rather than a merely representational, standpoint.

I took her designs for a walk round the garden. The lower croquet lawn was called SNP, and was to be turned over to a large planting of *Cirsium heterophyllum*, the Melancholy Thistle. 'Intensely loveable as symbols, and apparently charmingly architectural,' said her rubric. 'But doomed to collapse and infect large areas of marginal ground with seeds that look light and airy, but which show themselves after a couple of years to be a self-perpetuating disaster.' I spent a short time wondering whether it would be possible to play croquet in this deeply unpleasant entanglement, decided not, and moved on to the next spot, which was called the Labour Garden. This was to be sited in the Sunk Garden, where it is our habit to have lunch by a newt pool built along the lines of Lutyens's reflecting ponds in New Delhi. This she seemed to want to dig up and replace with a monoculture of *Salvia coccinea* 'Red Army Choir', from which would project here and there sanguinary maples. The green ink suggested that the salvias represented the masses, and the maples towering above them the fact that while all are equally red, some are more equal than others. Passing a hand across the brow, I moved away from this Socialist bloodbath and unfolded the next page of her scheme, featuring the Big Lawn.

It was rather unnerving. The peaceful, tree-studded sward was gone. In its place was a huge planting of gentians, interspersed with geraniums ranging from the pure sky colour of 'Buxton's Variety', via some magenta horrors, to varieties that were a congested and apoplectic black. A few mighty oaks remained. The ink said this was about Conservatives. The massed gentians were the unthinking we-want-it-like-it-was true-blue rank and file. The liberal wing was represented by the magenta horrors. Libertarians, who in countries less soothed by horticulture would be locked up as anarchists, were black. Party grandees, many of them cousins of the Duchess, were represented by the mighty oaks. Clambering into the lower branches of the oaks were some rambler roses – remarkably thorny, the Duchess pointed out, and with enough ambition to scramble their way just about anywhere; but genetically incapable of ever being truly blue.

I sat down on a stump, hyperventilating, and examined the last sheet. It was the Home Meadow, and it was little changed, except for some yellow wild flowers. I did not need to look at the scrawl to know that these were yellow rattle, parasitic, and symbolised the LibDems.

I tucked the designs into my desk and wondered what on earth I should do with them. On the one hand, they were ghastly, and would have a devastating effect on the pleasaunces and messuages.

On the other hand, a Duchess frustrated in her aims was a Duchess sulking, and a Duchess sulking is a Duchess walking down the long, woozy road to rehab. I poured a glass of strengthening Leoville-Barton 1990 and pondered. The evening grew cool, so I lit a fire. The following morning I discovered that the papers I had used to ignite the kindling had been the Duchess's designs. As the great Sigmund Freud said, there is no such thing as an accident. Sighing, I drank a cup of coffee and braced myself for the wrath to come.

The Duchess returned from her French jaunt looking bronzed and fat. I began haltingly to explain that the moth, or perhaps the mice, had got at her Political Garden. She waved me away. 'That old rubbish?' she said. 'So last year. Politics come and go, but a vineyard is forever.' And she launched into an explanation of her scheme for planting a couple of acres of some vine or other they had shown her in France. Digging her long red nails into my arm just above the elbow, she marched me outside to view the site she had chosen, gibbering in French the while. Then she came to a halt, her eyes fixed on the boundary, which was marred by a splash of purple and yellow. She said, 'What is that enormous bunch of deadly nightshade doing in the hedge? How odd that it is still flowering at this time of year.'

'That is not deadly nightshade,' I said. 'That is a UKIP poster left over from the euro elections.'

'Oh,' said the Duchess. 'Get rid of it, will you?'

It seemed that the danger had passed.

Blackwater Fever

UNSPEAKABLE. *Unspeakable*. Or so the Duchess was saying the other day. She was describing the weather, and incidentally speaking, so 'unspeakable' was not necessarily the right word to be using, but who was going to point this out to her on a day when she was wearing her rubies, so bad for her mood? Not me.

Be that as it may. The rain descends in the quantities known to French people as *halbards*. Vertical streams of water make bars on the windows at the Hope. The place where the ponds used to be before an agricultural neighbour bulldozed them is a sheet of water, on which ducks sport and play and in which parsnips occasionally bob past. And the mind returns to happier times.

The Duchess was very pleased this year to visit the Blackwater estuary in Ireland. This is a gigantic waterway that heads sixteen miles north from the town of Youghal, where in the garden of his house at Myrtle Grove Sir Walter Raleigh grew the first potato on Europe, or not. More recently, Molly Keane wrote a series of excellent novels dealing with the lives (bizarre, frankly) and times (long-drawn-out to an astonishing degree) of the inhabitants of the enormous Georgian houses that scowl at each other down the banks of the river. Disputes between neighbours were once lethal. At Affane, just upstream from Dromana, Molly Keane's Aragon, the last battle between private armies on (at that time) British soil was fought between Butlers and Fitzgeralds as recently as 1565.

Things have got matier since then. The houses are still carefully placed just out of cannon shot of each other, but artillery is no longer regarded as an acceptable means of resolving after-dinner disagreements. Naturally the Duchess does not approve of this softness, but she can be distracted by mention of Ducal links with the castle at Lismore, owned by the Dukes of Devonshire and built by (among others) the dream team of Joseph Paxton (exterior) and Pugin (interior). The Castle has a garden timed to peak in the spring, when the Duke pops over for a spot of salmon fishing.

Downstream at Cappoquin, the garden of the big house is also, the Duchess reckons, worth a dekko. It sits on a south-facing slope with a fine view of the river, and has an almost Bhutanese profusion of rhododendrons from December onwards. Many of these were planted by the late Olivia Keane. Sir Charles, the current baronet, has beefed up the plantings considerably with perfect globes of yew contrasting with Rococo sheets of Belgian hydrangeas and some odd target shapes mown into the grass. The target form, it turns out, is derived from the brass inlaid decoration of a box of Purdy duelling pistols in the house. This was most encouraging for the Duchess, in whose view, often expressed, gardening is too much about prettiness and not nearly enough about sex and death. Her enthusiasm resulted, indeed, in an invitation to drinks, which she was in the process of accepting when I hustled her away to the weird pleasaunces of Dromana.

The approach to this noble edifice, at first a castle, then a Jacobean house, then a late Georgian monster and now, thanks to dry rot, a Jacobean house again, is singular. The visitor drives along a narrow lane across a bridge decorated with a domed gate lodge in the Hindu Gothic taste. It was erected in *papier mâché* as a decoration for a Fitzgerald family wedding, and everyone liked it so much that it was reconstructed in stone. Dromana itself has been continuously inhabited by Fitzgeralds for eight hundred years this year. It sits on a crag above the river, and was once famous for its Hanging Gardens, maintained in the glory days by a small regiment of gardeners. These vanished under a grim tide of *Rhododendron ponticum*, but are being revived by Nick and Barbara Grubb, who found the original 1750 plan of the gardens and have attacked doughtily with Roundup (holes drilled downhill in any and every trunk thicker than your arm, poison poured in) and chainsaw. The Duchess found much to approve of, particularly the Bastion, an ancient boathouse with a lawn on top, approached by formal steps between two gigantic banks of gunnera. She was also pleased to see the Grubbs sploshing around in the mud of the river bank ('slob', they call it round these parts) netting salmon under a charter engrossed some years before Magna Carta.

From here we took ship to Strancally. This is a fine castle in the best tradition, with lawns sweeping up to walls of nineteenth-century vintage and noble trees in a Wodehousian park. It has recently been restored to something approaching brilliancy by a new owner. It is easy, contemplating its current splendours, to forget the dark rumours concerning the existence beneath the castle's lowest cellars of a drowning cave or cell, situated below the level of high water and communicating with the river, where Strancally's medieval proprietors chained up their rivals pending the rising of the tide. Another useful but probably inaccurate rumour (rumours grow like ponticums in the valley of the Blackwater) concerns an elderly proprietor early in the last century, when dank trees overhung the turrets, rain streamed through the roof, and there was a lack of funds for paying Florence McCarthy, the well-known grocer and wine merchant of Lismore. The old man, a widower, lived with his two aging and sharp-tongued spinster daughters in a state of great misery. His desperation reached such a pitch that he was driven to place a pseudonymous advertisement in the matrimonial columns of the *Cork Examiner*. 'Lepping Henry, good farm of land, seeks bride,' it said, adding a box number. He got two replies, one from each of his daughters.

I thought the Duchess would never stop laughing.

Well, all good things come to an end, and we returned from Ireland laden with salmon and cuttings. What we were not laden with was *Ligularia przewalskii*, because we had got hold of it on a previous visit. This handsome giant groundsel is a charmer in a wet spot, which is why we brought home a couple of its airship-shaped tubers. Its downside is that the tubers have fleshy roots that look like legs. Using these and a fiendish system of rootstocks, it has stormed through the policies at the Hope with the kind of energy normally shown by Himalayan balsam, from which the saints preserve us. We have just eradicated it by systematic digging, and even so we walk in terror of its elegantly-cut leaves showing up again in the spring.

Sorry. Winter is upon us, and in the long nights and short rainy days the mind can be seduced by inanition into emphasising the negative to an undesirable extent. So now the Duchess is in the library, leafing through William Robinson by the library fire, and we splosh daily into the policies with a chainsaw. The delight of planting trees is that in thirty years or so they do tend to grow a bit. The downside is that sooner or later they start growing in at the windows. The upside to the downside is that you can then go and cut them down, and plank up the American walnuts that have shown themselves surplus to requirements and make furniture out of them, and chop everything else into stove-sized portions and store them in a fine dry shed.

And then, tired but happy, you can schlep indoors, fall into a chair by the fire and ruminate on miscellaneous topics. Outside, the night is a cold wet blanket. But we don't care. Sooner or later it will be spring, and we can go back to Ireland and catch big salmon under the blood-red japonicas trained on the walls at Cappoquin.

Hedge Fun

THERE ARE THINGS in most gardens over which the eye skates hastily, seeking a more pleasing object. Over the years, though, the mind becomes inured to the horror, and the kindly brain blots it out, possibly using the same process as when James Bond, faced with a laser beam up the jacksie, holds his breath long enough to black out in Goldfinger's metalwork shop. Which is a long way of saying that the Big Hedge at the Hope, never a pleasing sight, revealed itself this January to have got properly out of hand.

The instrument of revelation was the Duchess in one of her moods. She had woken early and sober. I found her in her drawing room thrashing her way through a nurseryman's catalogue, brows knitted into a sort of Turk's Head above the bridge of her bluish nose. 'Honestly,' she said. I waited. Out it came. 'Why can't they talk *English*?' She batted the page with her earth-black, enamel-red nails. 'Myosotis, forsooth, *Forget-me-not*, damn them. Primula, *Primrose*, curse their hideous livers and lights. Lavandula, give me strength, *Lavender*, pox guzzle the brutes.'

'Anemone?' I said.

'Exactly,' she said, then, sensing that all was not well, fixed me with a piercing look. I ducked, unwilling to be burned to a crisp, and the gaze shot out of the window, setting fire to a branch on the far side of the lawn. Her scowl deepened. 'When,' she said, changing the subject on a dime, 'are you going to do something about that ghastly hedge?'

She was looking at the Big Hedge, of course (she has the true professional's sense of where to apply the electrodes); and it was impossible not to admit that she had a point. Nowadays it was not so much a hedge as a hazard to aviation. Somewhere along its length a small, charming rowan tree had over the years become a forest giant. Towering above it was a wych elm that had steadily defied Dutch bugs, drawing sustenance from an enormous root system that was draining nourishment from most of the kitchen garden. Bridging the gap between these Titans were several well-grown thorn trees, half a dozen elders, a couple of superannuated plum suckers and a ferocious entanglement of brambles, nettles and old iron hurdles. 'A Gordian knot,' said the Duchess, slamming a jewelled fist on the whatnot in the manner of Churchill deciding on the Second Front. 'Be Alexander.'

By this I gathered that she confidently expected me to go out and swing the sabre, conquering the undergrowth. This was the old oil and no mistake, and it would be useless to deny that it did in some measure mount to the head, if that is what oil can mount to. I left the room as if carrying through snow and ice a banner with a strange device, Excelsior. As the door slammed behind me I could hear the Duchess, at the catalogue again, calling down lightnings on a nurseryperson who had described a datura as a brugmansia. I tuned her out, and the thought-process resumed along more measured lines. Felled in the usual hack-and-topple style, the larger trees would have devastated an acre of land. It was tempting to get the Duchess to put her money where her mouth was and catapult her into the upper branches bearing a chainsaw. But there were health and safety downsides to this process, plus I was by no means sure I could persuade her to step into the size of siege engine needed for the catapult job. So I rooted round till I found the roamafone half buried in the right-hand polytunnel, and rang the tree surgeons.

One morning in January, several men in large boots and hardhats swung into the upper branches. Chainsaws howled. Kettles hissed over fires of twigs. Tea was drunk, sandwiches eaten and queen wasps discovered. By the time the sun sank behind the hill the hedge was a large pile of firewood and a larger pile of brash. The tree surgeons accepted a fat cheque and went on their way rejoicing, and we went in for our own tea, followed by cocktails, with tomato juice for the Duchess.

The next morning I was woken by light streaming in at the window, a sensation which had for some time been foreign to the Hope. Where the Big Hedge had formerly cast its lowering shadow, a vista stretched away across lawns delicately frosted under an orchard of leafless crab apples, whose remaining fruits were under attack from blackbirds and fieldfares now able to see them without the aid of infra-red goggles.

There followed days of stimulating bonfires, and nights spent poring over yet more catalogues to decide what to plant in the new hedge. Many of these contained only Latin names, but the Duchess had taken one of her braces, and puzzled her way through them without complaint. We were going for the full William Robinson, we decided, an infectious blend of the forest primeval and the forest domesticated. The rowan and wych elm and what have you would be allowed to come up from their roots, then hacked and laid to provide a framework for stuff like clematis montana wilsonii, vigorous as old man's beard, pleasingly scented and not, like other scented montanas, pink. The voids between the stumps, and the craters where the elders had been hauled out by the traditional tie-them-to-the-tractor-and-drive-away method peculiar to the Hope, would be intensively mucked. Then they would be planted with tough roses – a few rugosas to make toilers in the kitchen garden sneeze with their scent, and a few more of a scrambling remontant tendency, all of them guaranteed to provide nesting spots for birds while wafting a powerful niff downwind. The whole works would be allowed to clamber about on itself and should in time convert itself in to a species of linear thicket in which native plants would fight it out with their slightly more well-bred equivalents. As Robert Herrick did not say, a sweet disorder in the hedge will separate the lawn from the veg. We will subject it to a once-a-year hackback that will with any luck stop it coming in through the windows.

Not that we expect things to stay under control. Resolutions like these are smelted by the fires of laziness into 24-carat guilt. Fifteen years from now, the Big Hedge will once again constitute a hazard to aviation, filtering the breeze for delivery drones bringing stuff they don't want to people who can't remember ordering it. At this point, someone will no doubt be tipping blood and bone on the roots to make it grow higher. We won't care.

But that is for the far future. Now, the Duchess is confecting a planting scheme for the edge of the hedge, and has so far departed from her original crossness that she has decided that only a working knowledge of Latin will allow her to get the drop on the horticultural universe. Atropurpurea (she has been explaining, while her listeners nod patiently) means 'atrociously purple', 'alba' means 'white', 'sylvestris' means 'grows in a wood'. The gin lies untouched, the Capstans unlit. Her lips are moving, and beside the catalogue pile lie Hillard and Botting and Kennedy's Shortbread Eating Primer. Soon she will be fluent. Listen! There are the magic words. Linnaeus, you should be living at this hour! Lean forward to catch the drift of her murmurings.

Caesar sic in omnibus. Cotta sic in at. Peals of schoolgirlish laughter, somewhat cracked.

Oh, well. You can't win 'em all.

Touring the Fame Garden

IT HAS BEEN AN ODD SORT OF SPRING.. The frosts got to us mentally, I suppose. Even the sudden self-conversion of the wintersweet into a fragrant chandelier outside the kitchen window failed to convince us that as true-born Brits it was morally necessary to hang around straining the ears for birdsong. So we headed for Andalucia.

The important thing, as those who know the Duchess will readily imagine, was to keep her away from the festive crime bars of the Costas. To this end we took a remote house situated in a ravine down whose bed brawled a stream fed by the eternal snows of the Sierra Nevada. The botany of the area was the usual kind of thing. As the hills steepened, the olives stopped and the almonds started. *Helleborus foetidus* struggled out of dry banks, wild asparagus was chucking up its shoots (housemaid's horror, said the Duchess), and little wild cyclamens spread their hot-metal scent by sunny walls. Quite a lot of the vegetable kingdom, in short, was girding its loins for action, hoping it would not be gnawed by the oryxes that seemed to be the only mammals in the landscape, unless you count the Duchess, which not everyone does, and quite right too.

We paid a lengthy visit to the gardens of the Alhambra in Granada because the Duchess claimed that Mohammad ben Al-Hammar, first of the Nasrid kings, was some sort of cousin thanks to an ancestor who had striven in a harem. She impressed this fact on the horticultural staff of the Generalife in what she imagined to be Spanish. The head gardener, a kind and patient man, stood among his carefully topiarised *Cupressus sempervirens* – surprisingly effective, if somewhat knackered by overclipping – and politely attempted conversation. He seemed to be under the impression that the Duchess was making remarks about the orange trees planted in the little square beds, and admitted that they were stunted thanks to an accidental earthing-up which had left the surface of the ground five feet up their trunks. The sun beat down from a sky without clouds. Pigeons buzzed over beds of ornamental cabbages, pursued by the local sparrowhawk, as we wandered among tinkling fountains. We went to a café and ate baby broad beans, raw, with rough salt. It was perishing cold.

Refreshed, we left for the beautiful Mezquita of Cordoba, whose enormous number of columns, each (according to inaccurate legend) quarried from a different battlefield where Abdarrhaman (another cousin of the Duchess's, who if you believe her must be about three quarters paynim) scored a one-nil victory over the home team. The Abbé Prévost once observed that the Gothic cathedrals of France were forests in stone. If this is the case, then the Mezquita, with its intricate mathematical symmetries and red-and-white arches, is an orange grove.

Or so I mentioned to the Duchess, feeling rather clever. But her mind was elsewhere, and her tongue ran round the lips as if she was reflecting that while gin was gin, vino de Montilla, as drunk in Cordoba, was certainly wine. I therefore frogmarched her back up the sierra, where she fell silent. And before we knew it we were back at the Hope with suitcases full of pelargonium cuttings, including a double pink one that looks as if it would be right at home on the stage of the Moulin Rouge. By now spring had pretty much sprung, but the Duchess did not notice, because her nose was in the sales figures of her book, which were spectacular. When she looked up, I asked her what was on her mind. She told me that nobody had really come to terms with her new notoriety, and that, well, in short, why on earth did someone not plant her a Fame Garden?

A *what*? I said. She told me that I had heard, and that she wanted a lot of laurel for wreaths, a triumphal arch made of marble obviously, and a tree that would bear golden apples as found in the Hesperides, and what else could I think of? Well, I said acanthus, because it is all over ancient Greece and come to that the Long Border, where it is making like a Panzer regiment in a cathedral. She nodded absently and said what she really wanted was palm trees in case it became necessary for her to make an Entry into Jerusalem. Here I had the faint but familiar sensation that things were getting out of hand. So I said all right, as long as she showed people round it, knowing that this is something she hates. She said of course she would, and to get cracking and let her know when it was finished, and stumped into the Tower and locked herself in her room. Through the floor I could hear her reading extracts from the speeches of Cicero in a harsh cross voice.

It cannot have gone well, as a couple of weeks later, as the masons were finishing off the bas-reliefs on the arch, she burst from her room and roared off to (as it turned out) the pet shop in Builth Wells. She returned clutching a cardboard box that barked. and for two months she was seen no more, except as a hand creeping out of the door to retrieve packed lunches featuring surprising amounts of Pedigree Chum. Then on one fateful day in mid May she emerged to survey the scene.

The Fame Garden was there, of course, and quite impressive, having come largely from Architectural Plants of Horsham, purveyors of colossal vegetation to the nobility. She nodded, as if accepting a just tribute. Then she emitted a piercing whistle. At this point a Jack Russell terrier bounded from the house, bearing on its collar an odd apparatus with a horn. The Duchess pressed a remote control, and a voice came out of the horn. It seemed to belong to David Attenborough, though one could not be sure. 'Here,' it said, 'you are in the middle of one of the wonders of the Western world, celebrating the achievements of one whose family lies at the very roots of its culture. The pyramids of Gizeh. The Forum of Rome'. Here the Duchess thumbed a button and the voice stopped.

I saw instantly what had happened. She had trained the dog to lead visitors round the garden, and had programmed the apparatus on its collar to transmit information at salient points. I congratulated her, and she announced that the Women's Institute coaches would start to roll as from next Tuesday. Last time the WI came to the Hope there was some unpleasantness involving forced labour and a bullwhip, so I advised her to leave tour-guiding to the dog and embarked on the boat for a cruise of the gardens of Scotland's west coast, where the davidias would be at it and the scented rhododendrons of Arduaine perfuming the ozone. It was from Roger, who nipped in to mow some of the lawns in my absence, that I heard what happened.

Apparently two coaches turned up and disgorged ladies in Crimplene. They were at first surprised to be greeted by a small terrier speaking in a baritone whisper. Surprise rapidly gave way to the normal delight of English garden enthusiasts confronted with small dogs. The terrier said, 'Follow me'. The Crimplene squad followed, entranced. The terrier led them here and there, admiring the borders, in splendid heart, the incipient wild-flower meadow, and the horse pond, where the irises were doing their stuff. Soon it had them trained, and they were hot on its tail, like floral Zeppelins chasing a Sopwith Pup.

It was as they were approaching the Fame Garden when disaster struck. Dave the cat, who had been snoozing in one of the sheds, chanced to stroll across the terrier's bows. There was a ferocious yipping, and the terrier took off. Dave shot like an Exocet into the blackthorn thicket by the orchard. The terrier, less cunning, pursued him. And two coachloads of WI ladies, deeply imprinted on their new chum, galloped after them. It took (said Roger) two hours to get them ladies from there, and more sticking plaster than he liked to mention to staunch the bleeding. The dog went back to its lair in the Tower. Roger was going to go up and see if it was all right, but as he was rinsing the gore off under the outside tap a gin bottle whistled past his ear, so he decided to let well alone.

When I got back I asked the Duchess how it had gone. She said in a new, humble voice that everything had been fine, but on the whole she thought the Fame Garden had been a bit over the top. I said no, surely not. But on the whole I had to agree.

Anyone for Tennyson?

So THERE I WAS, on a day of suffocating heat, weeding the pond. I have mentioned this chore before, I know: a grimmish process, conducted in a pair of chest-waders designed for the pursuit of the salmon. Taking a heavy iron rake, we first remove the Australian pondweed, which produces a frightful barrage of methane, alarming the goldfish, whose species memories probably suggest to them that they are being bubble-netted by a flatulent humpback whale. Then, seizing a short sickle with a serrated hook bought in a shop in Lucca that specialises in ancient vineyard weapons, the operative attacks the bog beans.

These vegetables arrived twenty years ago in a car belonging to a marine biologist who wanted somewhere to leave them for a couple of months. He certified them non-invasive, and like idiots we believed him. Since then they have developed into a murrain next to which the Plagues of Egypt resemble the common cold. They grow in dense mats which succumb only to the most violent of attacks. Subtlety is wasted on them, and Roundup is cheating. It is a case of hack, knight, or be overrun.

Once this menace has been humbled, or anyway formed squares and is telling itself to fight to the last bean, it is time to start on the water lilies, whose roots are nowadays as thick as a weightlifter's thigh. There is always a slight whiff of cardiac infarction hanging round this effortful phase of the operation, and it is wise to take precautions. I had therefore swallowed an aspirin and was oxygenating the system with deep, healthy breaths when something like a bomb hit the water behind me. The shock was considerable. I have a dim memory of seeing daylight between the soles of my waders and the surface of the water, and the aspirin unswallowing itself. Then I fell to earth I knew not where.

When consciousness returned I was puzzled to observe an arm sticking out of the brown-clouded surface, clutching something. I did a lot of blinking. The limb looked as if it was clothed in white samite, mystic, wonderful, if somewhat crusted with filth. Did the spirit of Tennyson walk the Marcher hills? Or was it the lady of the lake, all right, pond, possibly Nimue in person? If person was the word for a being made of 100 per cent proof magic? Here I brightened. Perhaps she was going to bung me a magic sword that would once and for all show the bog beans who was boss.

But (you will not be surprised to hear) the spirit of Tennyson didn't, and Nimue it wasn't, and there was no magic sword. As the vision cleared I observed that the sleeve was not samite, but that weird greasy stuff they make Barbour jackets out of. And the sword was not a sword, but a bottle whose label bore the legend Plymouth Gin Navy Strength 100 Proof, which implied that it contained something other than magic, or at least not the Tennyson kind. I plunged wearily into the murky deeps, found a shoulder, seized it and hauled. And up, spluttering, came the Duchess.

At this point I would have quite liked to join Arthur on his barge and sail off to the island-valley of Avilion, deep-meadowed, fair with orchard lawns. Unfortunately there was no Arthur, no barge, and instead of the island valley there was a hedge of overgrown dogwoods masking a shed with a corrugated iron roof. So I compromised by asking her what it was this time.

'Hot,' she said. 'Wanted to cool down. I need water.'

This was excellent news. 'There is plenty in the taps,' I said.

'Not that kind of water. Water to float on.'

'Ah,' I said, dragging her out and hosing her off, and marvelling at the congruence of our thought processes. And the following day we set off for the Netherlands, where the Duchess got her fill of floating hither and yon thanks to a kindly young man with an open boat. We ate lunch in the charming café at the Botanic Garden in Amsterdam and admired the endangered cycads. We complained about some of the more adventurous plantings, which closely resembled silent migraines. We rolled past the Bloemenmarkt, now a grim linear clip joint specialising in bicoloured dahlias, black tulips, cyanide-blue roses and DIY windowsill marijuana kits. And finally, when the Duchess declared herself properly saturated, we climbed onto a train and headed for what in the Netherlands passes for the hills.

Here, in a green and hopeful valley of loess studded with beech avenues (felled by the Germans in the Second World War to provide a field of fire for their 88mm guns, and replanted by the dauntless Dutch the moment the last jackboot scuttled off the site) we visited the charming abode of Romke van de Kaa, once gardener at Great Dixter and later at the Duke of Devonshire's Lismore Castle (which puts him in good with the Duchess). Romke is an old friend and all-round good egg, and can be relied on to have excellent ideas about what will work in the garden. Several years before anyone else caught on to the wild-flower craze, he had grassed over his borders, mowed them, removed the grass, and sowed parasitic yellow rattle all over the place (*Rhinanthus angustifolia*, not *minor*, because the leaves of the former are elegant, while those of the latter are rather squalid). Ten years on, his meadow is gasping for nourishment, a kaleidoscopic joy packed with orchids, buzzing with small thises and infinitesimal thats. The begonia mob, given like all Dutch people to looking over the garden wall and delivering unsolicited opinions, are outraged; Romke doesn't care. The Duchess was thrilled, speaking of a return to the hay meadows of her infancy, ploughed up by the rapacious land agents to whom her useless relations had delegated the farming. It was, she said, like bulldozing cathedrals and using the debris as hardcore for a motorway. Here she began to look depressed, and her gaze wandered, settling at last on a bottle of Nieuwe Genever. I hustled her on to a train, and soon we were home.

There is already a pocket-handkerchief hay meadow at the Hope, on trend as ever. The new proposal, which has the Duchess's full attention, is to do something interesting under the trees flourishing in the dappled shade that has replaced the deep shadow of the giant hedge, now departed. To keep it ducal, we will plant it with wild strawberries. There will also be the descendants of the blue wood anemones that flourish in the timber around Lismore. There will be lashings of Siberian squill, the blue kind, not the silver; there will be primroses (there was an argument here; the Duchess insisted on a lot of glaring polyanthi until I reminded her of the horrors of the Amsterdam Botanical Garden, at which point she fell into a silence just this side of hostile). Forget-me-nots hung in the trees to scatter their seed hither and yon. Pheasants' eyes in the clearings. All that sort of thing. Much to do, much to do.

And now is the time to be doing it. For the year has marched on, and the days of pond weeding are long gone, and so are the swallows. We are sunk deep in the mists-and-mellow-fruitfulness department. The seeds of some chillies we bought in Sri Lanka five years ago are producing something so simultaneously fruity and fiery that it is hard to stop picking them. The damsons have been a black fury in the trees, the apples, Alfred Lord Tennyson would almost certainly have admitted, as good as any in the island valley of Avilion, where falls not rain, nor hail, nor any snow, lucky devils. Meanwhile out there on the hills the shadows are lying long and black. But we won't think of winter yet. Sufficient unto the day is the evil thereof. Onward, into the cold and dark.

Birth of a Sea Garden

THERE WE WERE, a small but select house party. Outside, there were clouds pressing down upon the frigid soil, darkness permeating every nook and cranny, while in the potting shed there writhed chill miasmas bearing fevers. There was also rain.

Clouds and darkness yield to infrared goggles, and fevers can be controlled with aspirin. But there is no answer to rain, except to think about something else. There we all were, then, gazing out of the morning room window and observing half-heartedly that whereas English people say it rains stair-rods, French people say that it rains halbards, but then again so what. We had ceased throwing playing cards into a top hat, and tired of betting on which raindrop would be first down the pane, because the Reflecting Pool had overflowed into the Sunk Garden, and the attention of the big money had shifted to which flower bed was going to flood first. Certain elements (no names, no pack drill) were casting longing eyes at the cupboard in which the gin lies immured, when someone said, well, what about jiu-jitsu?

'What about it?' said Erica, a slender person with (in a good year) just about enough strength to deadhead a lowish rose.

'Why,' said the enthusiast, 'instead of hanging around moaning about the weather, do we not turn this frightful wetness to our advantage?'

'Such as how?'

'Canals!' cried the enthusiast.

'What about them?'

'They carry the eye down vistas with the speed and elegance of a figure skater! Think of Versailles! Or in a more crinkle-crankle form, Bryan's Ground! The cascades of Castelgandolfo! A stone frog that spits a jet of water in a fifty-foot arc into a basin in which reposes a – '

'You have strayed from the point,' said a severe voice instantly recognisable as that of the Duchess. 'A frog, no matter how stony, is not a canal.'

It was generally agreed there was much in what she said. The enthusiast retired hurt. This was a relief, of course. Digging at the Hope in even the dry parts of the year can expose underground lakes. In a wet winter a stroll on the lawn can make it look as if the battle of the Somme has set in with unusual severity, so the thought of heavy machinery excavating canals is one that produces feelings of deep hostility.

We therefore played Sardines until dinner, and billiard fives afterwards. That night a northerly breeze swept the clouds away, and great sheets of stars poured over the horizon, and there began a week of snazzling frost. We rounded up various walking sticks and on the rink formally known as the big lawn played ice hockey with a tin lid instead of a puck. The crowd then buzzed on its way.

The only person who did not join in the above high jinks was the Duchess; and not, I am happy to say, for the usual reason, viz. that she was spark out on the Aubusson. As the floods subsided she could be seen wading to and fro with jam jars full of pond water, which she had taken to studying under a binocular microscope she had installed in the Tower. She began heating her rooms to appallingly expensive temperatures, so that the creatures lurking in the murk came to life. She attempted to precipitate early spawning in newts, and caused great confusion among dragonflies. She ordered ranges of new zantedeschias in radioactive hues from websites devoted to swamp curiosities. Just before the Council closed the last library in the county she forced them to find her thick volumes on the arcana of hybridising water lilies, and filled fat ring binders with notes.

Meanwhile the work of the winter continued. We did plenty of drainage, chased the surviving rabbits here and there, pruned trees into approved shapes, kept an eye on the cold frames, felt relieved that the sub-tropical plant craze had left us, and generally tried to inhale a bit of fresh air between nine, when the sun got up, and three, when the sun went down. Occasionally there would be a white frost, and the sound of the church bells would roll over the fields like a dustbin falling down the cellar steps. More often there would be a kind of brownish mizzle that smelled vaguely of pheasant shooters' cordite; and through it all on we soldiered.

During this time I scarcely saw anything of the Duchess, which was frankly a relief. Though it must be said that an odd atmosphere did from time to time pervade the shadowy walks and rides that surround the Hope. And the atmosphere, as so often, was down to her.

Part of it was an unwintry excitement, which I attributed to the studies abovementioned. There was another side to it, though: a dark apprehension, as if one of the lumps of darkness lurking round corners might turn out to be solid, and sally forth at her behest to biff the unwary stroller on the mazzard.

She was spending more and more time closeted in her room, her face illuminated by the screen of the portable computer. Finally she stopped coming down at all, and life was extremely peaceful. Then one day the telephone rang and a man with a Scots accent said, 'I am happy to say that your offer has been accepted.'

'What offer?' I said, feeling a chill.

'Ha, ha,' said the Scot cheerfully, and put the phone down.

Gripped by a wild surmise, I ran into the Tower and hammered on the Duchess's door. 'Offer?' I said.

'Go away,' said her voice, muffled by the two-inch oak. 'No. Wait. Accepted?'

Well, these one-word questions could have gone on all day with nobody any the wiser. I persuaded her to open the door, and found her scowling at her computer, on which glowed the words 'Cooking with Seaweed'. I said, 'Might one enquire what you have offered, and for what, and how, and why?'

'The sea is the ultimate aqueous environment,' said the Duchess. 'I have therefore bought a shed in Scotland. It contains bunks and a stove, and is by a beach. There is no garden.'

My gaze shifted beyond the window to the acres stretching away black and grim. That very morning I had been gazing at the geometry of the hoarfrost in one of those sempervivums with cobwebs between the leaf tips, and wondering a) at the beauties of nature and b) how much more of this we could put up with. 'No garden?' I said. 'You interest me strangely.'

'I shall start one,' she said. 'It will be fringed with a kelp forest studded with tiny bioluminescent crustaceans. Inside this we will grow sea lettuce and dulse for the kitchen. There will be a rockery of coldwater corals and sea anemones in variety. The tide-ripples will make Japanese gardens for us in the sandy patches. Fuchsia and tamarisk will admire their reflections at high water. Sea levels are set to rise by twelve feet in the next eighty years, according to NASA. By then they will be doing it in Norwich, not to mention Chelsea.'

'Marvellous idea,' I said, and I meant it. 'But now it is time to pack.'

'Pack?'

'We are going to Ceret in the south of France,' I said. 'The sea in those parts is full of good and interesting botany.' And on the land, I thought, the mighty Canigou, northeasternmost outlier of the Pyrenees, rises snow-capped above valleys pink with sheets of almond blossom.

I explained. 'Oh, all right,' she said, jerking the power lead of her computer out of the wall.

In spring, plan sea gardens. In winter, head south.

Glucose Magic

THE SPRING WOOD is working rather well. Since we took down the big hedge the light has come streaming through, and the grass among the intermittent trees is sending forth plenty of scillas and wood anemones and one thing and another (though not, alas, the bluish version that thrives in the valley of the Owenashad above Lismore Castle in the county Waterford, not to be confused with the nurseryman's too-blue 'Lismore Blue'.) The pheasant's-eyes are eying the sky, the *Magnolia stellata* is powering into action, and there is a general sense that any minute now we will be able to stop skating on the floods and start living again.

All this and much else should have produced a spring in the step and a glide in the stride. Other factors, however, intervened, and there was a moment when life took on its usual aspect of being roughly six to five against. The reasons, largely philosophical in nature, are as follows.

Scarcely had the Duchess and I scraped the almond petals from our boots after our sojourn in Ceret, France, when I heard cries of distress emanating from the Tower. Grabbing the telephone, I began to dial 999 as a preliminary to summoning fire, ambulance and clergy (the police would not have come). Remembering from whom the cries would be emanating, however, I stopped after the first 9 and sprinted through the connecting door.

The Duchess's ancestors goggled down from the walls, some manic, some bovine, some merely loopy. Their descendant was arced across the room in a curious rigid posture, a sofa arm under the back of her head and her heels on the carpet, but otherwise out of contact with cushions or floor. My first thought was strychnine, my second, infinitely more serious, gin. But when I checked the armoured cupboard in which the stimulants are stored, I was relieved to see the seals were intact. At this point she extended a quivering forefinger towards the telly, which was on. 'Animal,' she said hoarsely. 'Gibbering greenery yallery colour blind timid bourgeois moron'.

This kind of remark, undoubtedly illegal in the brave new Britain, is the common currency of this remarkable woman's discourse. I therefore paid no attention, confining myself to sitting on her until she relaxed a little. Once the vibrations had died away, I glanced at the screen. On it, a *soubrette* with big teeth and a fleece was talking to a man in tweed about gardens. The pair of them stood on a terrace overlooking a dullish Home Counties landscape, in the foreground of which a couple of borders were muddling their way towards a slot in some hedges. The woman waved her hands around in the odd, jerky manner of one with media training. 'So this is your garden!' she cried.

'Yes,' said the tweed man gloomily.

'It was designed at the turn of the last century for your grandfather wasn't it by a designer who was also a painter and very influential wasn't he and of course specified plantings in great detail didn't he and very lovely they are too aren't they in colours ranging from white to mauve spilling infectiously over the hard landscaping don't they which echoes the stone found in the surrounding hills doesn't it thereby integrating the surrounding countryside with the garden though of course the designer never visited the place did he how unlike the Victorians how unstuffy how free.'

'Yes,' said the tweed man, looking despondent.

'Bilge!' cried the Duchess, somewhat muffled by the sofa. 'Hogwash!' Classifying this as an overreaction, I did not reply.

The girl with the teeth was now banging on about colour in the garden. She appeared to consider it vulgar. Glory be to God, she seemed to be saying in a non-denominational manner, for glaucous things.

'Glaucous?' shrieked the Duchess, uncushioning her voice. 'Sugary tasteless stuff Nanny brings you with water in it when you are ill in bed!'

'You are thinking of glucose,' I said. But deep inside me, her outrage was finding an echo. As usual, the pundit was ignoring the joyous eruptions of Victorian fantasy, Gulf Stream-warmed, that sweep up the west coast of Britain from Tresco to Inverewe. And as the programme continued, the outrage grew stronger.

The teeth woman guided us past grey shrubs and grey walls,

speaking much, breathing little. Her view seemed to be that a perfect garden did not rock the boat, was incapable of causing offence, and was entirely inclusive, as long as what was being included was glaucous. Or to put it another way, grey. It was the horticultural equivalent of Orwell's newspeak, a language eviscerated to the point where it could express no view divergent from the orthodox.

Tweed man and teeth woman gazed moodily into a grey pond in which grey fish swam. 'Magic,' breathed the teeth woman.

Here I noticed that my own strangled cries had joined the Duchess's, and neither of us recovered until she had seized a log from the basket and hurled it through the TV screen. A silence fell, punctuated only by the insect tick of cooling microchips. And I knew we were both thinking of Augustus Smith, founder of Tresco, and Osgood Mackenzie, founder of Inverewe.

Under the gaze of these powerful characters the telly version of garden magic, based on fiddlings around in the Home Counties and the Cotswolds, more or less dries up and blows away. Augustus Smith founded Tresco in 1834, his avowed object being to harmonise with the surrounding land- and seascapes. He instituted a top terrace to represent heaven, middle terraces to represent the world of mortals, and mysterious walks, green and submarine with tree ferns and bamboo, at the lowest level. The story ends at Valhalla, a home for figureheads salvaged from Scilly wrecks, turtle shells, conchs, cannonballs, and other jetsam that would in the nature of things land up in Davy Jones' Locker. This, and the sun on his mesembryanthemums, some hijacked from passing ships' cargoes bound for Kew ('they would only kill them,' he used to say, swiping a few boatloads) produced plenty of magic.

Osgood Mackenzie was another visionary giant. He and his clansmen hacked the Inverewe garden from a landscape so bare that coffin planks had to be imported from the Lowlands. As for integrating the place with the landscape, it is possible to sit in his garden in exactly his seat and look through his own gate across his beach on to his loch, where the Great Northern Divers glide to and fro, yodelling defiance at suburban orthodoxies.

All this I said to the Duchess, who (for a change) agreed. The rain had stopped, and it was a beautiful morning. Into this we marched. 'Today,' said the Duchess, 'I will strike a blow for freedom of expression.' I noticed that overhearing this, some of the garden staff waiting for orders slid behind trees. 'Today,' said the Duchess, 'I will be planting lithospermums in an area cobbled with knapped white crystal pebbles. Nearby I will put in a late ceanothus with a rose 'Dutch Portrait' growing up the middle of it. The colours should be just about complementary, and the buzzing line between them should with any luck produce epileptic fits in amateurs of the glucose . . .'

'Glaucous.'

'. . . is what I said. Particularly,' said the Duchess, hope dawning deep in the slit-trenches of her mascara, 'if they work for the television'.

Staff wanted

'IF THERE IS ONE THING with which I cannot be doing,' said the Duchess, demonstrating simultaneously her vicelike grip of English grammar, her fluency in the demotic and her ancestral prejudices, 'it is lack of staff.' And actually for a change I knew how she felt.

Life has been moving crookedly at the Hope this year. The old plants still do their stuff in their allotted places. But certain things have changed – some for the better, viz. the old asparagus bed, dynamited after last season, is no longer the no-man's-land of twitch and creeping thistle that used to blight our days; and some for the worse, i.e. the *Daphne cneorum*, most splendid of its tribe, which spent years rolling in an odorous red wave towards a sort of ledge at the edge of its bed, now seems to have fallen over it and has vanished without trace. This is a big problem, given the suicidal tendencies of most daphnes, our lack of skill at propagating same, and the fact that fresh supplies of cneorum seem only to be obtainable from the geniuses at Burncoose, where it comes in at thirty-five quid a pop. Still, the Woodland Floor plantings did their stuff in the spring, and now tremulously await the first signs of the late-summer mowing.

Which is where the real difficulties come in. For while the weeds are being weeded and the plants tended with love and affection and all that, the heavier tasks about the place have somewhat fallen into abeyance. This is because Roger, who does the mowing and the chainsawing and annually cuts the hundred-yard fifteen-foot-high beech hedge round the kitchen garden, is not feeling very well, which he has a perfect right not to feel, because the first time he cut the hedge he was something over seventy years old, and that was ten years ago. But his absence, which we hope is strictly temporary, leaves a gap in the horticultural economy.

Actually it is not so much a gap as a thicket, in which brutal and low-grade things are overtaking delicate and beauteous things with the remorseless violence of Czech trucks gatecrashing the

London to Brighton Veteran Rally. I am not, of course, the only person to recognise this. The other day I was moodily practising croquet ap-proach shots on the hay meadow formerly known as the South Lawn when one of the windows in the Tower flew open. A hand appeared, the forefinger extended, shuddering slightly so the many rubies of its rings took on a sort of migraine shimmer. For a moment my heart plunged, and my hand went to the cellar keys in my pocket, seeking reassurance like a traveller in a haunted glen groping for his St Christopher medal. Still there. The shudder was nervous tension, not, as so often, gin. I relaxed, and asked her what was eating her.

'Stay,' she said. 'Stay, stay, stay, stay, *stay*.' My trained senses suggested to me that she was talking about stay. I was not wrong. 'Stay,' she said. I was about to mention that it is odd, the way a word can lose its meaning with constant repetition, and that per-haps this is where transcendental meditation, which as far as I can tell involves the repetition of a meaningless mantra, gains its mind-clearing efficacy, when she uttered a low, plaintive cry. 'The drive,' she said, her voice tumbling like a cracked bell down the slope of a buttress. 'When I was a girl the gardeners used to get down on their hands and knees an arm's length apart and crawl down the gravel of the Long Avenue, removing stray weeds with their little spuds. They were sixty abreast, and they moved at a mile an hour. It took them all day. How we used to laugh at them, the sillies!'

Forbearing to mention that this silliness was all that stood be-tween garden staff, dismissal, eviction and starvation, I affected interest in a plantain of surprising size. I would have to hear her out, in the same way that once you have started pouring treacle from a jug it is folly to stop before the jug is empty, as you get treacle everywhere, and everything is sticky for days.

'The staff we used to have!' cried the Duchess. 'McTavish!'

'Gesundheit,' I said.

'Ah, McTavish!' she said, ignoring the *politesse*. 'The Head Gar-dener! What whiskers, white and sweeping as the snowfields of Aviemore! What a suit of thornproof tweed, passed on by Great-Grandpa's valet! What a watch-chain!'

'And who else?'

'Under McTavish there were three Heads of Department. There was Enzo, who was foreign but he couldn't help it I suppose, who did the fruit. There was Nairn, who was a nephew of McTavish, who did the flowers. And there was Cyril Gumption, who did the vegetables. A bad thing happened to Cyril, because if he didn't win Three Good Turnips every year at the Show he would have been dismissed instantly of course, but he always did, and nobody could understand why until one year he was found suborning Mrs Rigby the Chair of Judges behind the Duck Tent. In Flagrante Suborno, Enzo called it.'

'What,' I said, 'is the Duck Tent?'

'A tent for ducks,' said the Duchess.

'And what was the bad thing?' I said, bracing myself for the saga of a husband dismissed and a family starving.

'He had to marry Mrs Rigby,' said the Duchess. 'Eighteen stone if she was an ounce. Stop interrupting. He lasted a year. Under the Heads of Departments were the Departments, composed of propagators, and planters, and pruners, and weeders, and diggers, and composters, and apprentices, and O'Riordan who used to put the shoes on the donkey before it mowed the lawn so the croquet balls would run true . . .'

Here I must confess I tuned out, because my attention had been caught by the *Trachelospermum jasminoides*, which seemed to be practically leaping up the wall. I had tripped over one of these ordinary but terrifically sweet-smelling climbers in one of the quads at Univ during a recent meander round Oxford. It is a couple of doors away from the odd but affecting memorial to Shelley, in this rendition hovering somewhere pretty central on the trans spectrum, by Edward Onslow Ford; and the combination is hard to forget. I was dimly aware of the Duchess's voice quacking away in the background as I meditated on the death of the poet, who as you will know drowned off Italy after refusing to reef his grossly overcanvassed boat, thanks, it is said by some, to the bad advice of Trelawny, a faux-pirate otherwise known as Lord Byron's Jackal; and contrasting it with the extreme civility of the gardener at Univ, who, when I enquired about the beautiful glossiness of the trachelospermum in the quad, offered me a cutting thereof so the true line could continue . . .

'So,' said the Duchess, counting on her fingers. 'That, with Mrs Maggs who made the tea, makes sixty-one in the garden.'

'I thought you said sixty.'

'McTavish never did any actual gardening.'

'So what did he do?'

'Sat at a desk in a potting shed and drank tea. At least he said it was tea,' said the Duchess. 'Though I always thought it smelled like whisky. Well, can't stand here talking all day. Time to get on with it.'

'Get on with what?' I said, realising with what you might call a sick apprehension that during the wanderings of my mind I had missed a significant remark. But too late, for the window had slammed, and she was gone.

The next thing I heard was the wheeze of a starter motor and the putter of an engine, increasing to a thunder as an unseen hand jammed the throttle on to the stops. Two minutes later a ride-on lawnmower hurtled round the corner on two wheels, the Duchess wild-eyed at the helm. She roared past me, spewing cut grass and shouting words that I construed as follows: 'If a job's worth doing it's worth doing yourself!' So crying she carved a green trench across the South Lawn and smacked into an apple tree. Smoke began to rise, quickly followed by the discreet orange lick of flame.

I had already filled the fire buckets. Picking up one in each hand, I began to stroll towards the wreckage. Staff, I was thinking. Staff wanted.

North!

IT FEELS AS IF it is being a funny old season. Partly this is down to the slightly suffocating effect of large quantities of mists, not to mention mellow fruitfulness. Partly it is down to the exhaustion produced by the tasks attendant on putting the Hope to bed for the winter – a bit of storage and jam making, a spot of planting, a certain amount of hustling the debris of fallen trees into the various sheds where they can lie until called on to burn or form part of the structure of the buildings. And partly it is down to what insurance companies probably call exceptional circumstances.

A dose of these turned up a while ago. I had been on the landing outside the Duchess's rooms in the Tower, reading (as is my habit) the science pages of *The Times* to her through the keyhole, when there was a noise as of a volcanic eruption, the door flew open, and the woman herself shot past me and down the stairs, shrieking, 'Quick! Hurry!' Pausing only to finish the crossword, I strolled after her. Sounds as of someone ransacking cupboards rose from below. Glass broke. Instinctively, I flared the nostrils for the doomy aroma of gin. But there was nothing spirituous about the vapours wafting from the depths. In fact they smelled more like gun oil. And I suddenly realised where she was.

With three great strides I was in the gun room. Sure enough there was the Duchess knee-deep in the remains of a glass-fronted cabinet, Purdey over one arm and in the other an object that I recognised as the Indian Army issue forked vermin stick Uncle Algy brought when he hurried home after the business with the maharani's purdah. 'What?' I cried. But she had brushed past me and was gone, scattering cartridges in her wake.

Bitter experience has taught me that it is no use following the Duchess when she is armed. One needs to take cover, find the root of the problem, dig it out, and patiently extirpate it before she can open fire, causing at worst death and at best high-branch pruning in the Home Wood. So back up the stairs I went, and collected the scattered pages of *The Times*. And there it was, large as life.

One of the stories I had been reading had concerned the diamond-back moth, which had apparently arrived from the Continent in its legions to devastate our broccoli. I smote the brow. To the Duchess, one of whose ancestors made a million in the negotiable affection sector in the mining camps of the California gold rush, a diamond-back means only one thing, viz a serpent some six feet long whose fangs spell death, or actually fangs, but you know what I mean. Hence the gat and the stick.

Sighing, I went after her, and found her crouched tensely by a medium-sized rabbit hole, safety-catch off, vermin stick poised. I began to speak in a low, tense murmur. Many hours later, I had lured her in to lunch. And shortly after that, we departed the Hope in search of the therapeutic effects of sea air and a snake-free zone.

We could have gone to Ireland. But the Duchess had heard rumours that prankish zoology students from Trinity are making ceaseless efforts to introduce snakes there, and she would not listen to my reasoned arguments concerning St Patrick. She did however agree that there are practically no snakes at Mount Stuart, one of the principal ornaments of the Isle of Bute; so it was thither that we proceeded.

We sailed into the harbour at Rothesay and approached on hired bicycles, the pistol-shot cracking of the Duchess's knees almost drowning her complaints. There is a car park, with buses and a visitor centre in the modern taste against one of whose walls is a splendid thicket of royal ferns. The Duchess caused the usual trouble at the ticket desk, first because she gets furious when anyone believes her when she says she is over sixty, and next because her own family has never got round to charging admission to any of their houses (though God knows they are a secretive bunch, and it would certainly help if they actually told someone where the houses are).

There is nothing secretive about Mount Stuart. The policies extend to some three hundred acres of woods, full, when we were there, of the foxy niff of over-the-hill azaleas. It is a fine collection of trees, but large, very large. Everything about Mount Stuart is large. The mass planting of phormiums is large, and so is the task of the three gardeners (out of twelve) tugging despairingly at the dead but still recalcitrant leaves. The kitchen garden is Brobding-nagian, and slightly (observed the Duchess, a captious critic) out of hand in spots – not because of any lack of effort by anyone, but because three hundred acres divided by twelve means that every man jack and woman jill of the staff has twenty-five acres to keep scrupulously tidy. If seven maids with seven mops swept it for half a year, do you suppose (the Duchess said) that they could get it clear? Shaking the head, we passed on towards the house.

This also demonstrates a tendency to be large, or indeed titanic, or possibly even gargantuan. There are those who admire the Gothic Revival, and fair play to them, as we say in Kington Rural, but as far as I am concerned it looks like Dracula's holiday cottage. The late-nineteenth-century Gothic bit is a mighty edifice the co-lour of dried blood. It looms between two charming white wings with flared slate roofs dating from the early eighteenth century. It has pinnacles, turrets, an aerial gallery round which Jesuits can creep at the dark of the moon (the Lord Bute who built the place was, like the rest of his family, an ardent Catholic), a chapel, a stunning Marble Hall densely forested with psychedelic columns, an early central heating system and a Victorian lift, both still in operation. All is beautifully decorated with carving and mosaic in the William-Morris-Mezquita-Vatican-Ravenna-heyday-of-em-pire-damn-the-expense taste. The Duchess looked rather approv-ing. I was less so, as I recognised in its pleasaunces, messuages, apartments and appurtenances the prototype for St Custards, where Nigel Molesworth spent his formative years as any fule kno. We looked for an observatory built to study worms, but it was not to be found.

The effect of the vast pile, the splendid trees, and the cricket-pitch-sized lawn with vistas of a blue blue sea was to calm the Duchess considerably. I was able to place her on the boat and take her floating up the West Coast to the primula kaleidoscopes of Gigha and Tayvallich, Ardmaddy and An Cala. In Arduaine, where the pine-scented breezes fluttered the handkerchiefs of the enor-mous *Davidia involucrata*, she seemed to achieve a kind of calm, and even seemed to be winking at the handsome mate of a passing steamer. Breathing more easily, we put the boat back on her mooring and returned to the Hope.

Where, as I said, there is work to do. Mostly it is in the beds, after about a quarter of a century in need of powerful revision. We will be doing some of this with the help of Paviour and Davies, an excellent nursery specialising in plants from South America. While it would be vegetable murder to plant puyas, which are best left to Tresco, they have plenty of other stuff – and common or rare, it always seems to be of miraculous quality. This spring we had from them *Philadelphus* "Snowbelle", a compactish, i.e., non-rank shrub of astounding whiteness. There is a downside, though. The Duchess, who has been humming sea shanties, says it reminds her of weddings . . .

She cannot be serious.

The Innocence of Pumpkins

IT IS WINTER. The trees are black, the sky grey, and Dick the shepherd blows his nail. But there are a few bright spots. One is that the enormous oak that blew down in the spring gales is now burning brightly in the morning-room grate, giving the lie to the ancient Herefordshire saw that lightning-struck timber never burns. The other is that the pumpkins have gone.

Not that one has anything against these hefty cucurbits. The sleeping-bag-swathed giants are always good for a laugh when they are hoisted out of the unclosable boots of the Ford Capris in which they are traditionally delivered to the veg tent at Kington (pop. *c* 2,000) Show. As a household, though, we grow them to eat, not show or carve into Halloween heads. Not this year, though. This year the seedsmen let us down. Your seedsman is precise about varieties of zinnias and sweet williams and most other things, but he seems to blow a mental gasket when it comes to pumpkins.

I should explain. Your finest domestic pumpkin, it has always seemed at the Hope, is a thing called a Baby Bear, roughly the size of a two-pint teapot. We also grow from home-saved seed a nameless bluish-green object which achieves twice that size, and while it lacks the Bear's flavour is popular because you do not get all that many blue vegetables, and the Duchess says it reminds her of that awful little Huysmans person who wrote *À Rebours*. Be this as it may, the blue thing has the innocent talent of coming true from seed. This year the Baby Bears entirely failed to do what it said on the packet. They grew to the size of junior hot air balloons, looked pretty much inedible, and in September were heading for the compost heap when the telephone rang –

A word of explanation. The reason I am going on like this is only partly to vent my spleen against mail order horticulturalists who should be buying new spectacles or maybe retraining as welders. The rest of it is an explanation of how we got where we landed up, and what the consequences were.

So. There was the portable telephone, ringing, and there was

your narrator by the pumpkin bed, and there grovelling among the
winding stalks was the Duchess. On the other end were some
Americans, who had rung to say that they were planning to descend
on us in late October. When I had made the welcoming noises and
passed on to the Duchess the news of their arrival, she asked where
they had been calling from, and I said, Martha's Vineyard.
Vineyard? she said, and a chill, I tell you, ran down my spine as I
sensed a quickening of interest. Too late in the year for a visit, I
said. Not at all, she said, how lovely Americans are with their
pumpkins (you see the connection?) and their fine wines. She went
on to explain that the cooling influence of the Polar Current ceases
somewhere round about Portland, Maine, and the Vineyard is
exposed to the warming influence of some sort of eddy of the
Gulf Stream. You know Americans, she said. Call a spade a spade.
If they say it is a vineyard, there will be vines. And if there are
vines, there will be a *vendange* with associated frolic. Let us (said
the Duchess) hasten thither and see what the local version of
Bacchus looks like.

I opened my mouth to put up a strong beef, then closed it again.
She has been off the gin for a longish time, and it is only the frustration of her lightest whim that will send her back into the
darkness that lurks among the bottles in the cellar. So there was
going to be no whim-frustrating from my quarter, and as for the
western Bacchus, we would deal with him when we came to him.

So there we were a week later, high above the Atlantic, commenc-
ing our descent into Boston Logan. The Duchess was picturesquely
if originally dressed in a cowboy hat and an oilskin affair that she
claimed was her wine tasting suit. After we had extracted ourselves
from Customs, which thanks to the Duchess's sartorial choices took
a while, we boarded a taxi and proceeded to the Vineyard. The
light was bright, the sky blue, and the air bracing with ozone as we
hummed down the blacktop to the house of the friends with whom
we were to stay.

The Duchess's nostrils were twitching, I saw, and a look of
puzzlement was spreading itself over her noblish features. I con-
cluded that this was because there was no whiff of fermentation in
the air. When we arrived and after the pleasantries had been

exchanged, she asked where the best wineries on the island were to be found. 'Wineries?' said our hosts, laughing heartily. 'No such thing. George Washington thought grapes would grow here, but he and many others have found they don't, not hardly. There are wild vines, sure, but nothing cultivated to speak of.' She pointed out of the window at two laurel bushes and a lawn oppressed by a tangled thicket of wild vine and kudzu, which seemed to constitute the garden. 'Have some gin?'

The Duchess had been looking somewhat poleaxed by these tidings, and I could see she was about to say something derogatory about a nation that called an island a vineyard and failed to organize anything except a sort of bramble bearing a berry resembling a sour bullet, and yes, please, make it a large one. It was time to head her off, which we did nimbly by introducing her to various people called Guggenheim and Clinton and Kennedy. When the jetlag had diminished we nipped here and there admiring the carpenter's gingerbread houses of the locality and the Japanese-influenced gardens running down to the lagoon at Tashmoo. The closest we got to the local Bacchus was a kind and sagacious Wampanoag Indian called Buddy, the favourite fishing guide of Keith Richards of the Rolling Stones. Guided by this genius we fished for enormous striped bass while Buddy turned up the local classic rock station to 11 and we had some coffee. And in the end, the Duchess seemed not to mind that wine and gardens took a back seat to the social life. Indeed, she flung herself into this with abandon, even finding time to take a kitesurfing lesson from John Kerry, who was taking a well-earned rest from his duties as Secretary of State. We heard her shouting 'Gosh, this is fun!', though she may not have been sincere, as she passed this enthusiastic remark while being dragged through the shorebreak flat on her face at sixty miles an hour. John Kerry, a nice man, was later heard to say that he would have preferred fifteen rounds with Mr Lavrov any day.

But by that time we were home, and the Americans came and went, carving the pumpkins en route, and as I mentioned at the beginning of all this, it now seems to be winter. The eye passes over the sere and molepimpled lawns to the landscape beyond. The Duchess is in a chair with her feet up, reading a book. I edge closer. It is Tim Scott Bolton's *A Brush with Brown: the landscapes of Capability Brown* (published, in case you are interested, by the Dovecote Press, £25). She is saying something about taking this up. Painting? I say, for the book is full of charming watercolours. No, no, no, no, no, *no*, says the Duchess. The improvement of landscapes.

My eye roves the distant prospect of the Arrow valley and the surly hills beyond. In my mind I hear the grind of earth-moving machinery, and look out at a sea of mud studded with transplanted dead trees, and am surprised to feel a sort of nostalgia for the innocence of pumpkins. I suspect I manage a sort of smile, but it lacks sincerity. For there is one huge thought in my mind, and it is this.

Here we go again.

Come to the Hedge

THERE COMES A TIME in the lives of all thinking people when we must reflect on what divides us. In the case of the Duchess and the rest of the population of the Hope in winter it is plenty of thick stone walls of the medieval persuasion, thank goodness. But now the lark is back on the wing and the snail ditto the thorn the safe spaces are no longer safe, and she roams the policies seeking whom she may devour. Last week, as I was contemplating a short stretch of newish yew, I caught wind of her (Chanel No. 5, stale face powder, notes of forbidden gin) and asked her if she was all right. She responded in the normal manner, asking me who I thought I was, Sigmund ruddy Freud, and furthermore why didn't I mind my own business? Sensing a frustration, I asked her if she fancied an outing.

Well, of course she did. But, she wanted to know, where to? Repressing the urge to tell her my name was not Thomas ruddy Cook, I groped the ether for inspiration, and found myself looking at the first golden shoot on a yew I had been quizzing. So I suggested that we go and look at some hedges. She said that sounded all right, if boring. I therefore took her off to view a few. We went west, and stumbled around in the maze at Glendurgan. We went east, and lurched to and fro in the maze at Hampton Court near London. We went to Herefordshire, and caromed hither and yon in the maze at the other Hampton Court, designed by the great Simon Dorrell of this parish. In each of the mazes the Duchess lost her temper and had to be physically restrained from hacking her way out with the pruning saw that is her constant companion. So I suggested we stopped our quest.

'Nothing wrong with hedges,' she said. 'It is these blasted mazes that give me the pip. Don't they know who I *am*? Anyway. Hedges. More of them.' Her eye strayed towards the cupboard in the corner where the Plymouth gin lies swarming with nectar and the Capstan Full Strength sleep in their fat white cartons. Hastily starting the car, I hustled her down the drive, on to the RMS

Scillonian and off to Tresco, where we admired the cyclopean slabs of clipped ilex that shelter that most paradisiacal of gardens. The Duchess allowed as how this was all very delightful, but she seemed to remember in her infancy going to stay with someone in Scotland who had a real hedge, not one of these trivial objects that really one would scarcely look for on a council estate with any pretensions to horticulture.

So it was back to sea, and up to Scotland, where the Duchess hectored the satnav until it brought us to somewhere called Meikleour, where there is a beech hedge nearly half a mile long and about a hundred feet high, planted by keen Jacobites in 1745. The Duchess said that she would rather someone clipped the thing properly, and I observed that there was no pleasing some people, and the conversation lapsed into the sort of stony silence with which we are all too familiar. It lasted until we were nearly back at the Hope and passing the splendid village of Brampton Bryan, in which there is a yew hedge of some antiquity, cut so it appears to be melting down the sides of the long stone wall behind which it is planted. Here the Duchess, who claims to have had a short but weird affair with Salvador Dalí, perked up noticeably, and began to talk to herself in a low tense voice about the glories of topiary.

I now began to worry that she would want to fill the garden at the Hope with yew peacocks and box buzzards. My own preference is for musical instruments, as seen at Baverstock Manor in Wiltshire, a tribute by Tim and Belinda Hextall to Dicky Hart, lead vocalist of the Pacemakers; but I knew the Duchess, being tone deaf as well as everything else, would not be having with anything of that kind. We would stick with hedges, whatever the cost. It was at this moment that there was a sort of purring noise in the drive, and a long German car scrunched over the weedy gravel, and a figure in an impeccable tweed suit glided forth and towards the front door, followed by two lissom young ladies chatting in what seemed to be Russian. Swift as thought I concealed myself behind a fastigiate poplar, for this was Harry the Hedgie, financier and bane of the locality. Soon, however, I saw Harry come out of the house, trailed not only by the young ladies but by the Duchess, who had a worryingly purposeful gleam in her eye.

Darting from behind my tree, I asked her where she was going. 'Flying,' she said. 'With that awfully nice young man. He is a Hedge Fun manager.'

'Not Fun,' I said. 'Fund.'

Too late. The Duchess was already in the passenger seat, the door had slammed, and I was casting myself into the ha-ha to dodge the sleet of gravel flung up by Harry's wheels. When the coast was clear I rose, disengaged an earthworm from the eyelid, and took a walk in the Home Wood, where the anemones were beginning to do their stuff. As I strolled I reflected that peace, perfect peace is found, men say, only with Duchesses far away. It was then that I heard the natter of a helicopter.

It came over the boundary wood flying low. It circled once, so close that I could see the Bermuda tan of Harry the Hedgie through the windscreen, the Duchess sitting beside him, jewels flashing as she made hark-forrard motions with her blue-veined hands. The chopper tilted, flattened, and flew straight and level towards the Caledonian Glade.

It was at this point that I realised what was happening. Plucking the telephone from my pocket, I dialled fire, ambulance, and (as an afterthought) clergy. Then I watched, horrified, as the helicopter flew along the line of Scots pines, rotors clipping away the topmost foliage.

It could not last. I clasped the head in the hands and averted the eyes. The clatter ended in a final bang, swiftly followed by another, louder. Sirens wailed in the distance. I walked slowly, as behind a catafalque, towards the plume of smoke. I had always known that something like this would happen. The flames were orange and black, roaring like a hungry tiger. I stood there, shaking my head with a deep, deep sadness not unmixed with relief.

'When you have quite finished making like Little Noddy,' said a voice from on high, 'perhaps you could fetch a ladder?' I raised my eyes. And there was the Duchess, hanging by her hands from a limb in the crown of one of the pines.

'Oh, God,' I said.

'What do you mean, oh, God?'

'Oh, good,' I said.

'Listen,' said the Duchess. 'When we have finished this little chat, perhaps you could get a ladder, because my foundation garments are on fire.'

Reader, I walked away. It was the Fire Brigade who wetted her down with a hose and brought her back to ground level. She came and found me in the wood, where I was watching a polyanthus open in a little medallion of sun. I said, 'So you would like some more hedges planted here and there.'

'Hedges?' she said. 'Can't stand them. What I would like now is a good long stay on the Pampas of Argentina, where a hedge is something you read about in books, if you read the wrong kind of books.'

'Ah,' I said. 'Goodbye, then.'

'What do you mean, goodbye?' she said. 'You're coming too.'

And I suppose I was.

On the Naming of Plants

IT IS GOOD AND HOT NOW, at least some days. The cherries are on the trees, the lark ditto the wing, and the sun is shining through the pink wine on the table. There is in short a general sense that God is in his heaven and all is right with the world. It has, however, been said and said truly by Robert Hunter, chief lyricist of the Grateful Dead, that when life looks like Easy Street there is danger at your door. It is hard to imagine that this *aperçu* did not come from someone who has spent time living with the Duchess.

Take the other week. There we were, sitting on the terrace at the Stone Table and allowing the morning sun to infuse the system with Vitamin D, when she started to scowl at the wall of the house. I turned to follow her eye, because stone scowled at by the Duchess has a tendency to melt and run. No melting was yet evident, but the plant that scrambles up the trellis was looking apprehensive. 'That thing', she said.

'What thing?'

'White flowers. Smells. Glossy green leaves.'

'*Trachelospermum jasminoides*?'

'It is not getting enough water. Although,' said the Duchess, with the smug look she gets when she has identified a sitting target, 'why people have to give plants these damn silly names is absolutely beyond me.'

I raised a debonair eyebrow. 'Trachelospermum is, as I understand it, composed of two words. *Trachelos*, Greek, is cognate with *collum*, which means 'neck', though fascinatingly enough it is also understood to mean the generative portion of the adult tapeworm. And *spermum* in vulgar Latin means 'seed'. *Jasminoides* means 'like a jasmine', which you can see, because while the leaf bears no resemblance to *Jasminum officinale* the flower and the scent are not dissimilar. The habit of combining Greek and Latin words to coin a single portmanteau name is I agree reprehensible, but Linnaeus, who presumably had something to do with this, was a Swede, with a quite understandable Scandinavian remoteness from the Classical languages at their purest. Proceeding to – '

'Oh for God's sake,' said the Duchess. 'If there is anyone in the universe as pompous as you I have yet to meet him.' I lapsed into a wounded silence broken only by the roaring gurgle of Her Grace hoovering up *café au lait*. I was unpleasantly aware that there would be more.

More came. 'I mean,' she said. 'This is all just plain stupid. Once, the naming of plants was a simple thing. Take fuchsias. There was Dr Fuchs, eminent German herbalist, and a fan of his wandering to and fro in South America looking for something highly ornamental from whose berries it might be possible to make jam. Admittedly the jam was pretty horrid, but bingo, Fuchsias. Likewise Dr Dahl, who is reputed with I know not what accuracy to have been seeking a starchy food crop on which he could feed the peasantry. And wham, Dahlias. The fact that there were flowers which instead of being treated as a side effect became the main issue is merely a monument to the appalling taste of your average horticulture fiend.'

At this point I interposed a remark in favour of *Dahlia* 'Bishop of Llandaff'.

'Tchah,' she said with a sweep of the arm that brought the wind of a knuckleful of diamonds to my brow. 'I am greatly in favour of bishops, as you know. I cannot however say the same for *Dahlia*s 'Badger Twinkle', 'Orange Turmoil' and 'Nuit d'Été'.'

I bowed gracefully, then converted the movement into an examination of my shoelace. It never does to let her know she has the upper hand.

'Furthermore,' she said, 'I find myself opposed root and branch to the lobelia, though I have no idea who Lobel might have been. Anything called 'Flamenco', 'Sunburst', 'Whopper Mixed' and 'Rosebud Tutu' cannot expect to be anything but a hissing and a byword among right-minded people.'

It is hard to imagine where she got the idea that she had ever had anything to do with a right-minded person. And I probably would have told her so, had a messenger not appeared with the post. She leapt on it with a glad cry, flinging aside anything addressed to me and scrabbling with stained and claw-like nails at her own envelopes, which mostly bore the impress of payday loan companies. Averting my eyes from the horrid frenzy, I fished a couple of envelopes out of the reflecting pool and slit them with my teaspoon.

The only thing of any significance was an invitation from Toynbee College, Cambridge, to dine at High Table. The Mistress of Toynbee is a reader of these essays, a woman of some erudition who has long expressed a wish to meet the Duchess. Hence the invitation, and the fact that a couple of weeks later we were tooling through the now somewhat overblown suburbs of the Fenland town. The Duchess was in a strange mood, part exalted, part bolshy, and I was glad that there was no gin in the car.

Toynbee is a women's college, founded by tough eggs in the late nineteenth century. The Senior Common Room is furnished in a severe Gothic style, the only modern thing on display besides a couple of the younger dons being an enormous table covered in drinks. Round this were clustered a large number of women in tweed wearing collars and ties and with trilby hats pulled firmly down to the eyebrows. The state of their fingernails persuaded me that this was an evening with a horticultural theme. I plunged instantly into a fascinating conversation about the species rhododendron in sickness and in health, but was distracted by a sight of the Duchess draining a glass of colourless fluid, smacking her scarlet lips and offering it for a refill. Any minute now she would be singing sea shanties. My heart sank, and I considered evasive action.

But at that moment a great gong rang, and we trooped through hundreds of seated undergraduates to the long table on the dais. The Duchess was seated at the right hand of the Mistress. I saw her reach for the wine and fill her water glass with it to the brim, and was then swept away by my right-hand neighbour. Though it was hard to concentrate, as I could hear the Duchess discoursing at high volume on the Naming of Plants. 'Bloody awful world,' she was saying. 'Daffodil "Hell in a Bucket". Helleborus "Grim Bastard". Paeonia "Mortal Wound".'

'Though it is interesting,' said the gruff if cultured voice of the

Mistress, 'that there is a class of insectivorae called Nepenthes. Nepenthe, as you know, being the original anti-depressant.

ἔνθ᾽ αὖτ᾽ ἄλλ᾽ ἐνόησ᾽ Ἑλένη Διὸς ἐκγεγαυῖα:
αὐτίκ᾽ ἄρ᾽ εἰς οἶνον βάλε φάρμακον, ἔνθεν ἔπινον,
νηπενθές τ᾽ ἄχολόν τε, κακῶν ἐπίληθον ἁπάντων . . .

Have you the Greek?'

'Only Prince Philip. Third cousin four times removed,' said the Duchess, mightily slurred. 'And never mind all your foreign nonsense. Give me Rhubarb "Death Trap" and Iris "Black Insanity".' Here, mercifully, she fell off her chair.

I will draw a veil over the next half-hour. Suffice it to say that she was borne, singing, back to the car by a corps of medical students, while the High Table tut-tutted in an annoyingly understanding manner. And a week later, when she was quite better, we were sitting at the Stone Table again, and she said, eyeing a 'Madame Alfred Carrière', 'D'you know, a rose by any other name would smell as sweet?'

I nodded, consumed with astonishment. Could this be penitence for her frightful behaviour? Then, in a sort of flash, I understood.

She was sickening for something.

Travels in Hibernia

Mists, innit, and mellow fruitfulness. Though the fruitfulness has been somewhat compromised by a severe lack of pollination caused by the agricultural community's campaign against all insects, nasty buzzy things, the farmers, not the insects. Butterflies? About three seen all year. Bumble bees? I spotted one just the other day, crawling round on the ground as if recently hit by a truck. So the long and the short of it is that anything bug-pollinated is in rather short supply.

There have, however, been triumphs. When we were in France during the month of February the Duchess persuaded me to buy in the market a pinkish object that looked like a cross between a hibiscus and a mallow. The vendor seemed to say it was called *Sminbodinpotheca dipsomania*. The man was a Catalan, though, and had what sounded like a speech impediment, besides which he was winking and directing the Duchess's vision towards the advertisements for cocktails lipsticked on the window of the Café des Ivrognes. So I bought it and ran, towing her behind me through the crowds. The thing has been flowering ever since, bless its scarlet spathe, if that is the word I am looking for. Catherine Janson, fount of all plant wisdom, at first identified it from a dodgy photograph as as *Althaea armeniaca*, though if this was so I have no idea why it has been flowering for so long. A better photograph changed the diagnosis to Anisodontea 'El Royo', and without one of these no garden of ours will henceforward be complete. We plan to make more, me by taking cuttings, the Duchess, more disingenuously, by returning to the original vendor, whose phone number she has got and who seemed to be a man after her own heart, assuming she has one.

This is all by the by, though, and based on observations made since we returned from a late-summer wedding in County Waterford. Of the nuptials themselves I will say little, except that the bride was lovely, the groom stalwart, and the Dean of the Protestant cathedral in Lismore in fine voice. We stayed for a week, and there was a party every night. In the daytimes we did a spot of garden visiting.

The Duchess, who is looking over my shoulder as I write uttering irritating little clicks of the tongue, tells me that I have already written about the excellent gardens of charming pink-washed Tivoli and its neighbour, Cappoquin House. I have also, apparently, had a go at Dromana, the ancient Fitzgerald strong-hold. But developments in this latter spot have been so remarkable that it is time for further discussion. (The Duchess has gone away, thank goodness.) Where was I?

Ah, yes, Dromana. The house, you may remember, has been in the family for eight hundred years. In its earliest incarnation it witnessed horrid deeds, particularly, it is said by not very reliable sources, during the lengthy and violent disagreements between the Fitzgeralds and the Butlers. The Butlers, tough eggs, came to stay at Dromana, and the Fitzgeralds, equally tough but bound by the ancient laws of hospitality, fed and watered not only the top Butlers but large numbers of their men-at-arms. After a few months supplies ran low, and the Fitzgeralds, concluding that their guests were taking the mick, slung them out, retaining only the head Butler. The rest of the Butlers now laid siege to the house, and said they would only go away if they got their chief back. The Fitzgeralds agreed, and threw him out of the main gate. In slices, via the letterbox.

True or not, this is the kind of story that really gets the Duchess's attention, so nothing would do but that we should revisit the gardens to see how things were developing. We were fed tea and delicious ink-black chocolate cake by the current chatelaine, Barbara Grubb, née Villiers-Stuart, herself a Fitzgerald. We reminisced about the enormous Georgian part of the house, long since demolished, which featured a huge circular drawing room in which Claud Cockburn, there for a hunt ball, noticed that people seemed rather thin on the ground, and remarked on the low turnout. He was informed that there were in fact four hundred people in the room.

A garden tour then commenced.

Ten years ago, the policies at Dromana were a howling jungle of oak floored with an impenetrable tangle of ponticum. Three years ago, on our last visit, the clearing was well under way. Now it is all but complete, and an eighteenth-century system of pleasaunces and messuages has clambered out of the strangling dark and been planted with stuff of which the eighteenth-century originators would not even have dreamed. Ancient and beautiful structures remain. There is the Bastion, a sort of subterranean boathouse from which stone steps rise flanked with self-sown gunnera once visible from space but now reduced to a more manageable half-acre or so. The stone for the Bastion was carved elsewhere and assembled on site, various bits being dropped in the river en route and lost in the mud, since retrieved and used as garden seats. (The Blackwater is a hungry sort of river. It is by this Bastion that one of the house's owners fell out of a boat with his pockets full of gold sovereigns. The money sank him like a brick, and he drowned. You could hear the Duchess laughing from the other side of the river, here roughly as wide as the Thames at Greenwich.)

Another ancient and noble structure is the Banqueting House, specially built for picnics. This was buried until recently under a vast mound of ivy and ponticum. Now the mound has been cleared and the trees that grew through what was once its roof have been felled, and it is the focal point of a splendid fernery.

There are new developments to match the old. Barbara has installed two fifty-yard herbaceous borders. An elegant rhododendron peculiar to the garden has been bred and called 'Dromana'. And at the end of a walk through enormous sweet chestnuts stands a recently-planted *Emmenopterys henryi*. This fine rarity, described by Ernest 'Chinese' Wilson as 'one of the most strikingly beautiful trees of the Chinese forests' is bounding with health, revelling in the mildness of the Blackwater rain forest. It may be thirty years before it flowers, but all are confident that it will be worth the wait.

As you will imagine, the Duchess took some dragging away from all this. But once the last cup of tea was drunk and the last barrel of wedding Guinness drained we were at last able to shoo her on to an aeroplane, and back to Blighty we flew. Since then she has locked herself in the Tower, complaining of a slight headache, and nobody

is all that surprised. Besides which, there are other things to think
about. The air is thick with the steam of boiling vinegar as fumaroles of chutney glug sullenly on the hob. Stuff is being dried and
boiled and jammed and bottled and the rest of it. And most
importantly, we are beginning to fit out a large sailing boat for
next year's extended horticultural voyage to the west coasts of
these islands. One of the advantages of this voyage will be that
the Duchess says her sailing days are over, so there is a chance of a
bit of peace and quiet.

Oh God. She's back, standing behind me as I write. How very
much I hope she will come too, unless of course she is put off by
the charming narrowness of the quarters, the exquisite
primitiveness of the sanitary facilities, the splendid roughness of
the seas, and the fact that the only drink on the boat is cool, clear
water in earthenware mugs.

How curious. It seems that these are all her favourite things,
too, and that what she hates most is loneliness and neglect. Now
she has gone off to pack. It looks as if she is coming along.

Ah, well. Worse things happen at sea. Not many, though.

Atlantis Ho!

So THERE WE WERE, hunkered down by a sullen wheezing fire, wearing three-piece tweed suits with double socks and extra jerseys. As you may recall, the spring and summer were wet, and come to think of it the same went for the autumn. The flowers did not, on the whole, approve, and rotted as soon as convenient, if not sooner. The trees, however, shot up like moon rockets. This fact made itself felt the other day when the Duchess, distracted from her usual occupation of laughing heartily at the Deaths in *The Times*, complained that she could not see to read. This was due, she further pointed out, to the number of branches that had interposed themselves between her newspaper and the dim grey light source formerly known as the sun. Why on earth, she asked, did someone not ruddy well *do* something about them, such as cut them off?

I suppose I must have made a remark about the many centuries of waiting involved in getting an oak tree to achieve a sensible size, and my reluctance to attack the policies with chainsaws. Whatever it was, she responded by striking a match and waving it in an ostentatious manner over what she was reading. Seeing that this was not having much of an effect, she then lit the paper. This provided a certain amount of light, but was self-defeating, in that the Deaths were consumed by flames, which proceeded via Forthcoming Marriages to lick at her bony fingers. I shall always remember the prismatic twinkle of orange fire in diamond rings as she flung the burning paper from her and into (as it happened) her handbag, which was open on the floor at her side. There was a dull boom as something in the reticule exploded. She maintains that it was a bottle of scent. She is deceiving nobody but herself. Bitter experience has taught me to identify the sound of an exploding hipflask at a range of fifty yards. Besides which I am intimately familiar with the smell of blazing gin, worse luck. Debris distributed itself hither and yon, burning with a strong blue flame. Before you could say knife the carpet was on fire, which was a pity, because it had been woven by nomads in Bokhara. The conflagration then spread to a grim darkish painting of boors revelling painted in the manner of Breughel *père*. This was not unwelcome, as the painting has been giving the pip to all beholders for many a long year. But there were principles at stake, so we did our reluctant best to save the thing.

A bucket-chain formed. Glittering fans of water sploshed here and there. A telephone call was made. Once the fire brigade had left, the Duchess made a determined assault on the moral high ground. Seizing a can of luminous orange spray paint she marched forth into the pleasaunces and messuages, and marked for destruction a lofty manna ash, a beech hedge a hundred yards long and fifteen feet high, and several other innocent trees. I followed at a discreet distance with a bottle of turps, wiping the paint off trees to which I had grown attached. She was entirely wrong about the beech hedge. In some cases, though, it was possible to see her point. The ash had caused a truly delightful *Acer griseum* to grow in a one-sided manner, and a *Malus spectabilis* had been writhing into the middle of a *M. transitoria* in a fashion both clotted and dismal. So up started the chainsaws, and down came several trees. The trunks went into the woodshed, and the twiggy branches found their way on to bonfires, whose smoke mingled with the drizzle in a manner frankly dispiriting. Winter returned. Nothing was growing, and all was slime.

It was at this point that I noticed the Duchess reclining by a window into which light seeped with slightly more eagerness than before the felling programme. She seemed to be thumbing through travel brochures. From my vantage point in the sentry box in front of the drinks cupboard I could see that most of them dealt with New Zealand. While I yield to none in my enthusiasm for Antipodean flora, particularly those that thrive among the bubbling muds of the North Island, I was aware that the budget would not stand a world tour. So I suggested the Canary Islands.

This went down like a lead balloon, as I had known it would. The Duchess made some remarks about beer-swilling yahoos and portable sunshine. As is always politic, I agreed with her. Then I pointed out that there were quite a lot of Canaries, and that in winter their climate was more suitable for walking than sprawling on beaches. And a walk can lead to some surprising discoveries. On Tenerife, for example, up in the eruption zone of Mt Teide where the Narices del Diablo exhale their sulphurous fumes, there is an extraordinary forest of green and black pines growing from hills made of broken-up lava the exact colour of red-hot iron. On the heights and steeps of La Gomera there grow several different kinds of forest, including giant tree heaths that extract their drinking water from the clouds that shroud them. Among these heaths the natives discourse in a language of whistles. Furthermore, I said, noticing a kindling in her eye, there is a theory, held admittedly by the barmier elements of the populace, that the Canaries are the relics of the lost continent of Atlantis. Earth, the theory goes, has had several successive moons, which over time come closer and closer to the planet's surface. As they get lower, the gravity of these moons counteracts the gravity of the planet, so it becomes weaker, and people are able to grow to enormous size. When at last the moon comes so close that it falls into the sea and causes frightful inundations, only giants standing on top of the peaks of the Canary Islands are able to keep their noses above water.

This theory is popular among right-wing lunatics. As such it should be meat and drink to the Duchess. I could see, however, that she was not exactly going to swallow it whole, and it was hard to blame her. I suspected that she would shortly ask a question along the lines of why, if this was true, the Dutch, most of whom live below sea level, were so tall; to which neither I nor anyone else has a sensible answer. So I changed the subject swiftly. During my forthcoming investigations into the flora of Gulf Stream Europe, I said, it would be important to track the sources of plants. The Canaries, and in particular Gran Canaria, are famous for the giant stonecrops known as aeoniums. Gran Canaria, I pointed out, is a nice place if you do not mind large arid landscapes, and has aeonium species by the score. Furthermore the sky is frequently blue and the yellow thing that rolls around it is called the sun.

The mascara-caked eyes rolled towards the window. A slug was making its slow way across the pane. Beyond it, smoke was seeping lackadaisically from a pile of *Prunus pissardii* branches and mingling with a clammy vapour that seemed to have seeped from a grim dank netherworld. Throwing a fresh chunk of *Fraxinus ornus* on the fire, I drew the notebook towards me and started to scribble. The Duchess rose, shook her head, and went to tear savagely at the door of the stout oak cupboard wherein repose the wines and spirits. 'It seems to be locked,' she said.

'True,' I said. 'And I have lost the key. But the wine of the Canaries, though sticky, is as famous as its botany.'

She sat quite still for a moment. Then she grunted irritably, saying Hah, or words to that effect, rose and left the room. As she left, she said, 'If you want me, I shall be packing.'

So it looks like the die is cast, and it is Gran Canaria ho. I hope this is a good idea. Somehow I doubt it.

Outshooting Farrer

IT IS BEING A QUIETISH SPRING at the Hope. The natural world, as usual at this time of year, is instinct with hope and joy. The daffodils, having stood with their noses in the air during weeks of snazzling frost and icy rain, ducked their heads and began to make like yellow bells with orange clappers. The cherries, which had been playing possum since they threw their leaves away in October, were detectably swollen in the bud. And the wild primroses seemed to be of the opinion that they had done their bit in the warm corners of the wood, and could now set seed and have a well-earned kip during the sweltering months to come. (Not very intelligent, your primrose, and notoriously weak in the weather-forecasting department). And the Duchess, living proof that every prospect pleases and only man (or in this case woman) is vile, has been pretty quiet, for her.

But it is said, and said truly, that after the calm cometh the storm. It broke one fateful morning when I was bunging in the traditional couple of rows of Arran Pilots, Good Friday being close at hand. As I shifted the bit of string from row one to row two I heard a harsh voice emanating, apparently, from the heavens. A raven? But the ravens only come down from the hills when the weather is cold, and it has been pretty clement lately. A chilly hand, I tell you, clutched at my heart, and I experienced a pricking in the thumbs, as if something wicked this way came.

Sure enough, as I raised my eyes to the source of the sound I saw pressed to the north face of the Tower a spidery figure in form-fitting tweeds and a climber's helmet, clinging to the stonework with fingers that twinkled with dirty diamonds. I passed a muddy hand across the brow. Perhaps this time, I found myself thinking, gravity would rid me of the menace – for menace it was, the usual one: the Duchess, at it again.

Aware as always of the precise moment at which she had become the centre of attention, she waved an imperious hand in summons. I repressed an urge to tell her that I was engaged in the urgent planting of spuds, so she could get her own dashed self down. Trudging to the ladder shed, I selected a longish three-parter, which I leaned against the ancient masonry. And up I went.

The Duchess was ensconced on a sort of ledge. As I approached she seemed to find something that interested her, and crept along the ledge, which was actually little more than a string course, in pursuit. I am not enthusiastic about heights, so I asked her with more asperity than interest what the hell she thought she was doing. She gave me one of her Looks, which can take the eyebrows clean off those unaccustomed to them, and said she was examining something. I asked her what. She said a plant, and sidled on, her blood-red fingernails making horrid scrapings among the self-seeded wallflowers and valerians with which all crannies of the Tower's masonry are infested. I asked her why she had called. She said she wanted to talk to me about something, she had forgotten what. I said that she had sounded as if she had been stuck. She asked me what in the name of hell fire had given me that idea, and would I mind shutting up, because she was busy. It struck me that she was winding herself up for what Dr Lu Ni at the Institute calls an Episode. So down the ladder I went, and moved it along a bit, and up the ladder I went again, with a view to sitting on a gargoyle and trying to talk her down.

By the time I reached her again she was in a sort of valley be-tween two roofs, from which she had cleared a clod of rotting leaves the better to examine a plant, using a powerful lens. Peering over her shoulder, I saw it was a houseleek or sempervivum. We encourage these, on the whole, as they are interesting manifestations of the logarithmic spiral, plus they protect the house against lightning.

'Fascinating, fascinating,' she muttered.

The roofscape of the Hope is somewhat unnerving. For one thing it is very high and very old. For another it resembles a small wild mountain range. Plants up here have a tendency to mutate, so *Lychnis chalcedonica* will change from its natural dayglo magenta to corpse-white and blush-pink, and sedums will grow to great size, the tips of their fleshy leaves linked by webs of greyish filament. It is all too easy to imagine animal genetics also turning weird, so that from behind a steep-pitched gable there might emerge a thing that is a cross between a cat and a bat and an octopus . . .

'Well,' said the Duchess. 'I have finished.'

I expressed my delight, and asked her what was the main thrust of the day's research. 'Alpines,' she said. 'Absolutely fascinating. Growing on slate and tile, minimum nutrients, hardy little devils, wild as anything, admirable, admirable. We should grow more. Many, many more.'

Well of course she had a point. I reminded her that the great Reginald Farrer had sown alpines in the cliffs above Ingleby by loading his shotgun with their seeds and blasting away at the otherwise inaccessible crags. She nodded, that dreadful absent look coming into her eyes. 'Shotgun,' she said. 'What kind?'

'Twelve bore, I suppose.'

'Pathetic,' she said, and shinned down the ladder with the *espiéglerie* of a circus aerialist.

A week later, I had forgotten the whole business when from the approaches to the Hope there came the grind of big diesels. Before I knew what was happening three sand-coloured Land Rovers had hurtled into the drive, disgorging men in battledress. They saluted the Duchess, who was standing on her balcony in a regal manner, and retired to the West Rockery. Here they started shouting at each other in a military fashion. After an interval the Duchess strolled out to greet them, wheeling a barrow full of parcels. When I attempted to follow, a sentry told me that he was establishing something called a perimeter and that I needed the password, which of course I did not have, so I went off to do some experimental and probably doomed pruning on some geriatric hebes.

Curiosity, however, got the better of me. Summoning up my Boy Scout training, I entered dead ground (the Sunk Garden) and approached below the skyline formed by the Wobbly Yews to a point of vantage (the Collapsed Medlar) from which I had a good view of the Rockery. Imagine my horror when I saw the Duchess pouring seeds into the nose of what was unquestionably a mortar bomb. One of the soldiers took the bomb from her and dropped it in the firing tube. There was a sharp chemical *thud*. Into the air the bomb soared, down towards the roof it fell, and over the ridges and valleys and turrets it exploded, shedding alpine seeds in all directions and precipitating an avalanche of unmoored tiles. Reginald Farrer, I thought, you have much to answer for. I leaped out of cover, barged aside a sentry, and stormed the mortar position, sending Special Forces personnel flying like nettles before the slasher's slasher. Reader, I deserved a medal. But as the Duchess's eye settled on me I knew I was going to get the opposite. Raising the arm as if to ward off a blow, I reflected as follows: perhaps soon we will live in a house covered in alpines. After its recent mortaring by the SAS, it will certainly not be covered by anything you could call a roof. But in the final analysis, life goes on.

If you can call it living.

Poisoning Canaries

ANYONE WHO HAS READ THE MINUTES of the meeting of the Hope Policy Committee held earlier this year may remember that it was decided that we should spend some time on a botanical expedition to the Canary Islands. This was a bold decision, taken in the face of previous experiences not altogether positive. Among the cloud forests of La Gomera, for instance, we once took a pre-Sunday-lunch walk on which we got lost. This became apparent as we moved from handhold to handhold on the sheer face of a ravine. Far below, a flock of birds fluttered above a waterfall. I pointed out to the Duchess that this was perhaps the last flock of real canaries in the wild, and she told me to shut up, and we carried on climbing. We did get back in time for lunch, but on Monday, not Sunday, having lived during the interim on *gofio*, parched maize meal moistened with thin soup, and slept under a tree.

We tried again on Tenerife, selecting a hotel that turned out to be wrapped in chilly and impenetrable cloud. Above the clouds we strolled among black pine trees growing out of rust-red lava, inhaling great draughts of sulphuretted vapour from a pair of fumaroles known as the Devil's Nostrils and contracting a cough that has never really left us.

But the urge to see aeoniums growing on their native cliffs once again proved stronger than the lessons of experience; so this year we decided to go to Gran Canaria. The Duchess did what she called research, vanishing into her quarters in the Tower and emerging to tell me that her results showed GC to be a tiny island, basking in guaranteed sunshine and the smiles of its charming natives. Not a tourist spot, she said, with a faraway gleam in her eye. The real Canaries. It was therefore a bit of a shock to turn up on an enormous island and find ourselves driving down a motorway on which most of the best-part-of-a-million inhabitants were driving in all directions to thousands of multi-storey hotels, or perhaps they were car parks.

Into the mountains we went, travelling at roughly the same speed as the rain clouds thundering down an icy wind from the north-east. We were staying in a charming and only slightly leaky villa, in whose garden oranges in variety, assorted proteas and two gigantic Norfolk Island pines grew with cheerful abandon. This brought the light back to the eyes of the Duchess, who had hitherto had a lowering look. After a quick burst of fever, which coincided with a gale that wrecked large numbers of boats in the island's marinas, we set out botanising.

With the Duchess, a botanical expedition is simultaneously a picnic and no picnic. The picnic part of it is accounted for by vast loaves of native bread stuffed with the pale cheese and oversalted ham of the country, swiftly thrown away by the discerning. The no-picnic element is caused by the ferocious scowl with which she views the undergrowth, as if seeking items of litter left by a head gardener the worse for drink.

What she was really seeking, though, were immigrants. The native veg consists of plenty of euphorbias, echiums, argyranthemums and so on. But Gran Canaria has been colonised by various interlopers, human, vegetable and indeed animal. Its often precipitous volcanic hillsides are studded with non-native agaves, interspersed with bramble bushes of doubtful provenance and an invasive yellow-flowered foreign oxalis wearying to the eye and not susceptible to eradication. Around the roots of this lot hop introduced rabbits, winding through a nightmarish throng of albino California king snakes descended from escaped pets. The snakes should in an ideal world control the rabbits; but the world is not ideal, and the snakes prefer to snack on the Gran Canaria Giant Lizard, which is being driven to extinction, while the rabbits, unpredated, eat everything green they can find except the oxalis.

After a bit of this the Duchess was beginning to get cross. So we wound past many hilariously arched *Agave attenuatas* into the high high mountains, and some 6000 feet above sea level found a village of housefronts arranged along a lane. The housefronts, it turned out, were the company entrances of caves. One of the caves was a restaurant, and into the gloomy interior we plunged, ordering up a couple of platefuls of the chickpea stew known as *garbanzada* and some blackish wine. Much heartened by this, we debouched into the afternoon and struck off up a footpath that wound into a glen heading higher into the hills. We found ourselves on a sort of heath, which petered out in its turn, yielding to sheets of naked rock. And there, glowing green in the middle of one of those sheets, lit by a single beam of sun that lanced out of a rent in the clouds in the style of the apocalyptic painter John Martin, stood a perfectly ordinary specimen of *Aeonium arboreum*, high above the limit of its traditional range.

Suddenly the airports and the motorways and the steady drip of water through the villa roof seemed worthwhile. I stood, jaw swinging, like Stout Cortez silent upon a peak in Darien. But silence never lasts long when the Duchess is around. 'Been here, done that,' she said, turning a grumpy 180°. 'I wonder if there's any more of that wine?'

After this, of course, it was necessary to head her off, so we shot downhill, where in a maze of lanes we discovered the Botanic Garden.

Normally, botanic gardens are about as interesting as encyclopedias, i.e., if you are very bored or have a use for them, fine, but if you want them for anything but reference or the relief of tedium they should be passed by with the light laugh. The Gran Canaria version is, however, something special, and enabled us to sort out and categorise some of the wild things we had seen growing on the island. The Canary Islands pride themselves on their dragon trees, *Dracaena draco*, odd objects with yucca-like tops and dropsically swollen trunks that prove irresistible to the graffiti carver. These and many other native plants are arranged up the side of a ravine. On the flat at the bottom of the ravine is an impeccable and romantically-arranged layout of plants native to all Canary Islands, featuring a hugely impressive selection of euphorbias.

Euphorbias are one of the Duchess's favourite plants. This is probably because most of them exude a poisonous sap, which causes blindness in humans and death in fish – to the point where in Ireland, members of the gardaí can be found lurking in a good patch of wild spurge near a salmon river, ready to nab an enterprising pool-poisoner as he gathers the raw materials of his lethal trade. The Duchess chose this moment to point out to a coachload of Chinese tourists that in case of snakebite – here she pointed to the pale form of a king snake slithering away under a boulder – an incision should be made in the crown of the victim's head and spurge latex poured into it. I was going to point out that a) this would sting like fury and that snakebite was probably a more desirable option and b) that king snakes are resolutely non-poisonous, but by this time the Chinese had fought each other to be first on to their coach and were hurtling into the offing, uttering harsh syllables of encouragement to the driver.

The Duchess, meanwhile, was lost in admiration of her spurges, mentioning the distinctive organisation of their leaves, in rows along the shoots – a characteristic visible in wet-weather examples like *wulfenii*, staples of the northern European flowerbed, if (said the Duchess) you really must; but also present in vestigial form in the vertical trunk and branch ridges of the huge succulent trees of the Southern drylands – an example, if any were needed, of the extraordinary adaptive powers of life to climatic conditions.

Or so the Duchess said. But then she noticed that the sun had come out, and claimed that she was getting thirsty, and not for a nice drink of water either. Water, she said, has got that horrid water taste, and there was something in her voice that spoke of Plymouth gin and improvised sea shanties and sweet brown tea in police cells.

It was definitely time to go home.

In the Northlands

'Sometimes,' said the Duchess, tweezing a tick out of her pale thin leg, 'you have to wonder about Scotland.'

I did not ask her what on earth she was talking about, for sometimes these pronouncements mean nothing, and sometimes they mean so much that the listener feels impelled to run off and lock himself in the potting shed for a day or two to consider the ramifications. This time, though, it was easy to divine her meaning.

We were sitting on a crag overlooking Loch Coruisk on the Isle of Skye. Loch Coruisk is a place which looks as if the Creator had dug his fingers into an unsuspecting chunk of landscape and pulled it apart, allowing millions of chilly gallons of water to flow in from the slopes of the Cuillins, most saw-toothed of Britain's mountains. The Creator then appears to have dusted the boulders off his hands and strolled back into the clouds, of which there is never any shortage in these regions. And there we were, contemplating the results, which with their crags and waterfalls would have given Caspar David Friedrich the creeps.

'I really do not know,' said the Duchess, continuing, 'what people see in this place.'

I was going to say that Dr Johnson had similar thoughts, but by this time the Duchess had looped the abseiling rope round her skeletal frame and was descending the cliff in a series of huge gawky bounds. When she reached what in these parts passes for level ground, she gave the swift tug on the rope that liberates it from its belay, coiled it briskly and set off at a jog-trot towards Loch Scavaig, the bay where our ketch lay anchored. The fact that this left me at the top of a fang of rock flawed only with the smallest of hand-holds did not bother her, and I worried that she was going to seek her ancient remedy for the *cafard* in the shape of a bottle of Auld Grimshader.

All such thoughts were, however, removed from my mind by the necessity of descending the crag, which I did with relative success, falling only the last twenty feet. Any pain or indignation I might

have felt was rapidly eclipsed by my noticing, where I lay on the
swampy ground, something that was unquestionably *Saracenea
purpurea*, an American insect-eating plant now naturalised in the
Highlands. This specimen looked in the best possible health,
which was not surprising, as it had made its home in the middle of
a cloud of midges that must have been the insectivore's equivalent
of a Lord Mayor's Banquet dished up punctually four times an
hour.

I limped back to the boat batting the air and shrieking slightly,
to find the Duchess, unaware of the combination of the lock on the
spirit locker, stone cold sober and laughing heartily at the large
red bumps adorning my person. She herself seems impervious, and
perhaps even toxic, to midges, and actually enjoys them because of
the *schadenfreude* produced by the sufferings of her more succulent
acquaintance.

On and on she went about the shortcomings of Caledonia. I de-
fended the place, being somewhat Scots on my mother's side, but
it was no good. Eventually I managed to divert her to the inquities
of all foreigners, and dozed off. Next morning I piled the climbing gear into its chest, hauled up the anchor, and pointed the boat's
nose south.

Over the sea to starboard lay Canna, the site of a once-fine
garden now blighted by salt gales and officialdom. To its south,
wrapped as ever in a broil of fume, was Rhum, seat of the eccentric
Mr Bullough, who was also a gardener on the large scale, but whose
conservatory, once home to hummingbirds and ornamental alliga-
tors, blew away in one of the gales that howl down the central glen
of an island so savage that its red deer have turned carnivorous.

Round the lonely peninsula of Ardnamurchan we sailed, a pod
of minke whales between us and the westernmost lighthouse on
the British mainland. Into Lochaline we went, to have a look at
Ardtornish. This is a garden recently retrieved from wilderness
by Faith Raven. In the castle's enormous polices mown paths
ramble among embothriums and skunk cabbage. The only disap-
pointment (expressed, naturally, by the Duchess, whose negativ-
ity was succumbing to horticulture, but only a bit) was that the
remarkable contorted elm I have visited on many occasions had

succumbed to the beetle, or old age, or something, and is nowadays a sad white corkscrew skeleton by the path from the anchorage to the kitchen garden. Then out we sailed down the Firth of Lorn, and were blasted by the tide through Cuan Sound, at whose eastern end a slender tower rises from trees.

Entering Argyll from the harsher world to the north has much in common with pushing open a gate and strolling into a walled garden. Beautiful oakwoods clothe the slopes that roll down to the sea, framing noble houses built a hundred years before Balmoral thrust the cod-baronial into fashion. At the foot of the slender tower is Ardmaddy.

This is a garden built, by the look of it, to proof the castellan against siege. It is a beautiful compromise between gastronomy and ornament. A large part of its centre is occupied by vegetables, with (the Duchess claimed, unable to hide the approval in her voice) six varieties of potatoes, and beans growing up tepees made of hazel wands united with miles of string. The whole garden is walled, enormously so, so the breezes from the sea cannot blow the plants out of the ground. And on the walls, against a backdrop in season of chocolate-scented *Clematis montana* var. *wilsonii*, grows a selection of Chinese lanterns and grevilleas and other stuff (said the Duchess) you would probably see in Cornwall or Ireland or somewhere like that.

The chatelaine of this spot had her head in a bush and her bottom in the air and was weeding with a friend. She accepted our compliments, and said we ought to go and see An Cala, by Easdale. The tide was wrong for sailing to Easdale, so we crossed the sea loch and walked a couple of miles. There was a school, and a turbid patch of sea over which we had sailed the previous day. Just past the school was an anonymous gateway, with a small sign announcing that this was indeed An Cala, and that the garden was open. In we went.

An Cala is an Arts and Crafts garden, descending in a series of terraces towards the sea. Which is like saying that the Tour d'Argent is a chophouse in France. Parts of it are beautifully formal. A path winds up a cliff face behind it, giving a view of the whole. Candelabra primulas in carefully-chosen psychedelic colours flower along the base of a terrace with a pond and a kiosk exquisitely decorated with patterns of pine cones and branches that has all the beauty of the Shell House on Tresco, but which given the nature of its constituents cannot be more than a temporary decoration. And at the garden's southwestern corner is a border of such enormous size, kaleidoscopic brilliance and botanical joy that all the Duchess (who made the remarks above) could do was stand in front of it with her jaw swinging.

'Well?' I said. 'What do you think of Scotland now?'

She was drawing breath to repent of her harsh words when I noticed a small man standing in her shadow. He was shaking his head. 'Aye,' he said, in the accent of the region. 'It is a thing, a thing, all right.'

'What is?'

He gestured across the garden wall to an enclosed expanse of water that stood between us and the sea. 'The slate quarry,' he said. 'Ah, vanity, vanity.'

'What?' said the Duchess.

'Twa hundred feet deep, it was,' said the man. 'Came a night mebbe a hunnert years ago, a high tide and a southerly gale. Dozens of men working doon there. The last thing they saw was the waves overtop the quarry's edge. Then doon came the watter, cold and green, and not a man of them survived. There they lie,' said the small man, 'to this day.'

'Gosh,' said the Duchess. '*That's* more like it.'

The Exterminating Angel

IN THE AUTUMN we looked out of the window and observed that it seemed to be raining, and that the wind was blowing violently in all directions. We had just visited the excellent Picton national collection of Michaelmas daisies in Colwall, near Malvern, and there was something peculiarly dispiriting about watching several hundred quids' worth of *Aster novibelgii* performing cartwheels in the yard before they landed in the pond, where the heron used them for a raft from which he could harpoon the remaining goldfish.

I was leafing through *Cahiers du Cinéma* in front of a smoky fire when I saw an advertisement for a film festival: a real one, lively, in a place where the browsing and sluicing would give us strength for the cinematic ordeals to come, not to mention the howlings and freezings of winter at the Hope.

I metioned it to the Duchess. She said, 'Where is it?'

'San Sebastián,' I said. 'Quite close to Biarritz.' (You will observe my cunning. It is one of her favourite notions that she used to nip down to Biarritz to play whist or snap or something with the Prince of Wales, not the present one, of course, but the one before that or even, when she is really misty-eyed, the one before the one before that).

'Hmm,' she said. And there it was, settled.

So a few weeks later we flew to Bilbao, where we dropped in on the Guggenheim Museum. I will not go into what happened there, except to say that Jeff Koons's ghastly *Puppy*, a gigantic dog coated with bedding plants, was at the time bearing a hideous and frowsy-smelling selection of Busy Lizzie and marigolds, to which the Duchess took exception, and which she attempted to replant with more discreet subjects after overindulgence in the tasting menu at Dando la Brasa. There followed a distressing chase, followed by a midnight taxi ride after which we found ourselves in San Sebastián, an interesting town, particularly if you are enthusiastic about the *pintxos* or tapas in which the bars of the place lie half-buried.

Around us the visitors to the film festival surged – small people, mostly, dressed in black and speaking a great deal of Spanish, mingled with expressive hand gestures. After a while I perceived a frown beginning to make crevasses in the Duchess's well-bred brow. I refrained from asking what was wrong, because it was nearly time to go to the first film.

'Franco,' she said.

'I beg your pardon?'

'All these little people.' She waved an irritable hand at the black-clad hordes. 'Like little fascists. How well I remember them – '

'Goodness,' I said. 'Is that the time already? We'll miss the film.'

'– hundreds of the little brutes,' she said. 'And Franco himself the worst of the lot. He used to come here for the shrimping did you know? Had a holiday home. We went to stay with him once. A cortège, really, from the middle of Madrid. Three identical Mercedes limousines with blacked-out windows so nobody would know which one to blow up. On every rock along the way a *guardia civil* with a rifle over his back and one of those ghastly patent-leather hats on. Like garden statues, really, except you don't get statues that smoke.' She paused, and I could see that a smoking statue was on the cards for the Hope, largely because she thought she would be able to sneak out and bum cigarettes off it. 'And then there was his house. The Miramar Palace.' She gestured across the bay at a stockbroker-Tudor edifice of some size. 'Awful place. And the garden.' She did things with her eyebrows. 'A lawn, and a lot of not very interesting trees, and a weird sort of mixture of palms growing out of hydrangeas, I ask you.'

'Oh, dear,' I said, watching the door close behind the last cinéaste, and the ushers lock it from the outside and put up a sign saying FULL in Basque.

'Do you know,' said the Duchess, 'I would really like a glass of wine?'

'Ah,' I said, and took her for a walk on the prom, where the tamarisk trees have been pruned into standards. This may be so the primeval fishermen of the town can weave their long thin twigs into lobster pots, though if you can find a primeval fisherman

among the joggers and valetudinarians on the prom in San Sebastián I will give you a pound.

'Franco,' said the Duchess. 'Awful little man in creaking leather
with cigarette breath.' She eyed a passing cinéaste, who was
dressed in the inky rigout of his class. 'And it is not as if fascists
have disappeared. I always say,' said the Duchess, who is always
saying something, 'that gardens should be autocracies, not dicta-
torships.' I said I did not know the difference, concealing the fact
that I did not really care either. She said, 'An autocrat is someone
like Joseph Paxton or Augustus Smith of Scilly. A dictator is
someone like the National Trust. Autocrats know what they want,
and make sure they get it. Dictators start from a wambly kind of
political idea like freedom of choice or total equality and end up
making something that looks like the boring end of Kensington
Gardens on a Tuesday in March. I *hate*,' said the Duchess, 'the
National Trust.'

Well of course she and her large cousinage have all given turreted
houses and broad acres to that splendid body of pasteurisers and
homogenisers, so she cannot be expected to feel any love for them;
particularly when the NT has turned the nursery into an interpret-
ation centre and tarmacked the maze. Looking at my watch, though,
I observed that we were about to miss the next film, so I suggested
that we make tracks towards the theatre. She came, complaining
that her feet hurt, and that the only thing that would sort her out
was a jolly good walk.

As we arrived at the theatre the FULL sign was going up again,
so we set off up a sort of hill on a peninsula in the middle of the
town's fine yellow beach. At home just now there is a strong movement to replant endangered black poplars, and we have stuck half
a dozen truncheons of this swamp giant into the boggy bit of the
New Wood. Imagine, then, our pleasure when we found the entire
hillside densely forested with them. We sat under their grateful
shade speaking of this and that, and it may have been the pintxos,
or it may have been the interrupted night, but we fell into a healing
doze. From this we woke some time later, to see that the sun was
low in the sky and that its beams were lancing across the bay on to
the inland mountains. These were covered in pine trees, and should

have been green. They were not. Great rusty patches had spread up their sides, and I realised with a lurch of the heart that we were in the presence of the horned beetle that carries the nematode *Bursaphelenchus xylophilus*, which originated in the far east and is now threatening a million acres of *Pinus pinaster* in the north of Spain.

This would have been enough to put the bastard child of Pollyanna and the Dalai Lama in a bad mood, so we went down the paths of the mountain arguing about the usual subject, viz. which was the most beautiful of Britain's trees. Predictably, the Duchess plumped for the Wellingtonia, though of course it is a) not British and b) not beautiful. I argued strongly for sycamores in spring, when their leaves are fresh and bright, and sit on the branches in exquisite sprays that look as if they have been cloud-pruned by angels. There was a disagreement that lasted an unspecified length of time. And as we descended the hill at a run, we saw the last blackshirt file into the auditorium, and the little man come out and yet again put up the FULL sign on the door.

'It's all right,' said the Duchess. 'We've seen it before.'

'What was it?'

'One of those Buñuel things,' she said. '*The Exterminating Angel.*'

'Of course it was,' I said.

Then we came home.

Timberrrr!

THE HOPE, where we live and have our being, has sat since the fourteenth century on a sort of platform of land hacked out of the rolling hills of northwest Herefordshire. At the western margin of the policies, overhanging the steep edge of the platform, the potholier-than-thou drive and a Primitive Methodist chapel, is a beautiful grove of wild cherries, *Prunus padus*, which in season transform the place with their blossom into a sort of junior Alps. Your cherry, however, is a short-lived tree, and this lot were planted during the last big makeover of the place, in 1919. They have put on a foot a year, and are now authentic forest giants.

I should say were, not are.

Wait for it.

The Duchess has recently surfaced from a trip to Sicily, during which she saw plenty of small dark people she described as 'cousins' and while nobody was looking tasted many of the local wines. It has been noticeable to several recent visitors to Sicily that the shotgun is being gradually replaced by the credit card machine, and the sights, while pretty much as they have always been, have a slightly less mouldy and crumbling air. In Palermo, for instance, the Dungeons of the Inquisition have been spruced up, the desperate graffiti of the heretics preserved, and the channels that used to drain the blood from the torture chamber given a good scrub. You can take tours, with charming and knowledgeable guides. ('Pity,' said the Duchess.) It is fair to say that nobody can do much to brighten up the catacombs on the other side of the city, where the dead lie incorrupt but pretty dashed alarming; but even there things seem crisper and brighter. ('Disappointing,' said the Duchess.)

Anyway.

The Duchess returned from her Sicilian adventure in one of those everything-must-go moods. Several innocent shrubs were given the US Marine pruning (short back and sides, and hell, take the top off too). Members of the family seeking to complain found

themselves addressing empty space containing only a volume of
air writhing with the turbulence caused by a Duchess whizzing
off to cause trouble elsewhere. When I finally caught up with her,
she was among the cherries (see above) with a man called Dave and
a faint aroma of gin.

This was not a good sign. The gin speaks for itself, and on occasion the Duchess. As for Dave, he is a V-shaped individual of
great personal nimbleness who works as a forester and Man of the
Woods. Most of his life is bathed in the howl of chainsaws as he
hacks swathes through the blackish and illimitable Sitka forests of
the Welsh Marches. Frankly I have always thought that the Duchess
had a bit of a fancy for him. Today his hardhat and the Duchess's
foul old Locke's trilby were close together, and for a delirious moment I was able to fantasise that we were in for a rerun of Lady
Chatterley. This would have been excellent news, liberating her
Gobelin-hung apartments in the Tower and freeing us to pursue a
life unworried by the prospect of her nicking the key to the drinks
cabinet and launching herself at the gin; but alas the heads drew
apart, and hope faded. Dave's was shaking. The Duchess's was nodding. A conclusion, one sensed, had been reached. The Duchess
explained the matter of their discourse, for Dave is not an articulate
person, and anyway it is impossible to interfere with Her Grace's
flow of speech.

She had never, she reminded us, liked the Methodist chapel, and
she liked it still less since someone had converted it into a weekend
cottage. Methodists were nearly as bad as communists, and people
who lived in towns and had weekend cottages were much, much
worse, why she could not precisely explain but there was no reason
why she should do any such thing, it stood to reason, that was all,
shut up, and do not stand there opening and shutting your mouth
like some kind of ruddy fish. She also knew that cherry trees can
contract a bit of rot through a crack in the bark at their bases,
which will then rush up inside the trunk, causing a constitutional
weakness that will bring them crashing down in the next fresh
breeze. On top of neighbouring weekend cottages, if any.

So was that, I asked, not a bonus as far as she was concerned?

Of course it wasn't, what did I think she was, Hermann Goering, running round dropping trees on people's houses? And stop saying but. DO NOT SAY BUT. Destruction was something she was in favour of, as any fule kno. But it must be creative destruction. So let it rip, Dave, she said, turning to Dave.

Let what rip?

But Dave had already jerked his start cord, and her answer was drowned in the howl of the saw. Almost immediately tall trees began to fall like rain. I went away, leaving the field to the Duchess and the Husqvarnas, and visited the memorial service of my friend Michael Black, sculptor in stone and causer of stimulating trouble. In the University Church at Oxford we remembered this genius and gardener, who recarved the heads outside the Sheldonian, and who after one bumper mulberry harvest by his studio at Wytham put on an elegant white suit, decorated it all over with huge crimson patches of squished berry, and set out on his evening's entertainment.

When we returned from Oxford the cherry trunks had been hauled away for planking, their attendant brambles had been torn out of the ground, and where once a mighty copse had stood was brown earth, featuring half a dozen unrotted trees and the tyre-prints of many tractors. I went to mourn, being still in a memorial-service frame of mind; but a strange thing happened. As I stood, head bowed, under the much-diminished canopy, something golden crept over my boots. It took a couple of tries before I recognised it as a sunbeam – and this in a wood where no sun has penetrated these many years. Light and air were getting into the hitherto motionless deeps of the thicket. And suddenly I knew what had to be done.

On those steep slopes where once the cherries rotted, we are planting up something that will be halfway between Mount Fuji and Bhutan, with perhaps a touch of the Appalachians thrown in for good measure. We will cover the ground with wood anemones and primroses, and plant flowering cherries and those beautiful double philadelphus from Chile, and even the odd rhododendron and bamboo. Up the remaining trees we will shoot 'Rambling Rector' and 'Paul's Himalayan Musk', and for good measure some clematis, probably *C. montana* var. *wilsonii* because you can't have too many. Then round about the equinoxes we will watch between the serried trunks and fronds as the setting sun paints the sky — you can actually see it now, the sky, that is, not the sun — blood-red and heaven-gold, something we have never been able to do before. And every spring the remaining cherries, uncrowded and majestic in their hale old age, will blow white and glorious in the balmy airs, watched by the entire family, who will be full of fine foods eaten round kitchen tables made from planks milled from the butts of the trees. To everything, we will tell each other, there is a season: a time to plant, a time to fell, all that.

And what about the Duchess?

Glad you asked. After very little thought we have ordered her a new drinks cabinet. It will be made of cherry wood by the finest craftsman in the Marches, and it will have no door.

Towards Valhalla

'IT IS TIME,' said the Duchess this spring, 'that we went to Tresco again.'

Of course she had a point. The *Malus transitoria* that is the Hope's principal ornament at that joyful season had duly bloomed into its snow-white galaxy, and shed its petals, and was pupating its thousands of tiny yellow applets, beloved of fieldfares and similar if we get a winter this year. The spring stuff, in short, was coming to an end, and the summer stuff was taking the deep slow breath that prepares it for the dive into the world of air. Plus nobody had been sailing for absolutely ages.

So down to the sea we went, and found the yacht *Dahlia*, pride of the fleet, in such beautiful early-season condition that even the Duchess, schooled among the brass buttons and close-seamed duck canvas of the Royal Yacht Squadron, could not but approve. I reminded her of the remarks of Joshua Slocum, the early solo circumnavigator, who said that he had painted one of his boats until he scarcely knew it from a butterfly. The Duchess, who had now taken surly at the lack of White Ensigns, observed that Slocum was some sort of American as far as she knew, though she did not much care, he being dead and good riddance, and the Squadron was the Squadron. I reminded her that until recently there were no ladies' lavatories at that august club, the female companions of members being forced to relieve themselves in the shrubbery. And we sailed, in a state of mutual recrimination from which I was only saved by the Duchess instantly being sick.

And sick she continued until I decanted her on to the quay at New Grimsby, capital city of Tresco. She clutched one of the granite blocks from which the landing is built, and for a moment I thought she was going to take a grateful bite out of it, like a Pope arriving in Ireland. This proved not to be necessary, which was a relief, because dentists are in short supply on Tresco. And on we proceeded to the New Inn for a refreshing ginger beer.

The anti-emetic properties of this handy beverage soon asserted themselves, and the Duchess started to look around her. 'Charmin'' place, I always think,' she said, and I could see we were on to a winner. 'Very tidy, for somewhere thirty miles out into all that unpleasant sea.'

'That,' I said, 'would be because of Augustus Smith.'

'Because of who?' she said.

I did not correct her grammar, for I was feeling charitable, and besides, one of the purposes of our visit to Tresco was for me to give a lecture on the life and work of this doughty Victorian, and I needed a rehearsal. 'Augustus Smith,' I said, 'was a young man with plenty of money, who in 1834 bought the lease of the Isles of Scilly from the Duchy of Cornwall, who had allowed the islands to become more or less derelict.'

'Same old Duchy,' said the Duchess.

Her views on the Duchy's landlordly qualities are her own, and she is never worth arguing with, so I proceeded. 'In the social sphere,' I said, 'he reformed the farm leases, which had become hopelessly entangled by a system of inheritance that had left some of the inhabitants with half-acre plots divided into twenty or thirty bits, some an hour's walk from each other. He also instituted education by charging island children a penny a week to go to school and twopence a week not to go to school; and banned the burning of turf, which contained most of the island's topsoil, on pain of eviction. Most notably for our purposes, he did a lot of building. One of his projects was Tresco Abbey, and thither,' I said, 'we will repair.'

And thither we did, strolling up a long drive past a body of water practically covered in waterfowl of a deeply unfamiliar nature. There were trees on either side, *Cupressus macrocarpa* and *Pinus radiata*. Shelter belts are crucial on Scilly, where the breezes regularly top seventy knots, and they are often replanted. Augustus, who found the islands bareish, began the process, filling the pockets of his convex waistcoat with gorse seeds, which he stuffed into the ground as he walked his policies. In the shelter of the gorse, according to legend, he planted the trees that are the ancestors of those under which we were now walking.

The object of this was not only to improve the agriculture of the islands, so the inhabitants were able to substitute decent bread for sea beef, otherwise fiendishly chewy limpets knocked off the rocks; but to shelter a garden. The island had once been home to a Norman abbey, and the monks, ever keen on terrestrial comfort before arriving in their heavenly home, had chosen for themselves a south-facing valley properly watered. Here Smith blasted his terraces and started planting. Several species that thrived on the mainland never properly achieved dormancy in Tresco's virtually frost-free climate, and died of exhaustion. An *Agave americana ferox*, however, destined for the conservatory of the baronial house Smith was planning by the old abbey site, thrived in the open ground when let out of its Wardian case. After this, Smith began a splendid sub-tropical collection, on at least one occasion hijacking a shipload of mesembryanthemums bound for Kew, at that time run by the great Hooker – a strong character, but not quite as strong as Smith. Hooker wrote to remonstrate. 'He would only have killed them,' said Smith, tossing the letter aside.

As I conducted the Duchess up through the old garden entrance and into the patch known as Mexico, where the puyas breed via blackbirds whose heads they dye gold with their pollen, I noticed that she had gone strangely silent. 'Something wrong?' I said.

She shook her head, wordlessly, for a change.

'The late Peter Clough,' I said, 'the Head Gardener of Tresco who went on to Gigha and Inverewe and is the editor of the seminal *Gardening on the Edge*, the last word on plants for tough but sublime spots by the sea, had a theory about Smith and his garden. I have touched on it before. He maintained that it was a sort of neo-Platonic scheme of symbolic levels. On the top terrace stands a mighty head of Neptune, once the figurehead of the steamer *Thames*, presiding over plantings of silver trees and other proteas, with glimpses of his watery kingdom in all directions. This, said Peter, should be regarded as heaven, abode of the Gods. Then a mighty granite stair descends past the Long Walk and the abbey arches and oddities like Smith's patriotic Union Jack garden, all very human and (if I may venture the rather voguish term) quotidian.'

'You may not,' said the Duchess, and I could see her point.

'Anyway. Below this we enter paths that wind through ferns and bamboos under the weird moiré patterns of dicksonia tree-fern fronds. The light is dim and submarine, and at the end of the windings we reach the loggia known as Valhalla, where the pillars bear figureheads from ships wrecked off Scilly and elsewhere. Nowadays the figureheads are restored and brilliantly painted, and have a sort of fairground gaiety. When Smith began them, though, they were as they had been dragged in by fishermen and wreckers, ground and battered by the death-agonies of the ships that bore them. Among them in the loggia lay old cannon balls and conchs and turtle shells Smith bought from the dozens of German ships that used Scilly to sit out the Franco-Prussian war of 1870. Valhalla is in short Davy Jones's Locker, where the mysteries of all this sea debris will lie unsolved until the Last Trump wakes the Kraken and its sisters.'

'*Much* better,' said the Duchess. 'You know, I think I could manage a cocktail?'

'Goodness,' I said, looking at my watch. 'It is time, I fear, for my lecture. Will you come along?'

'I think I've heard most of it already,' said the Duchess.

Reasons to be Cheerful

THIS AUTUMN we have been looking for reasons to be cheerful. And there are plenty of them, if you take the view that every prospect pleases and only man (in the old sense of the word, which is neuter, ergo not gender-specific, and signifies all humanity. Got that, girls? Fine) is vile. Even the apparent failures, such as the asparagus, which did not like the cold spring, resented the dry summer, and is now turning a sullen gamboge in the pretty ordinary autumn, have their bright side. I hesitate to go too far into this, limiting myself to the fact that the Duchess calls the stuff Housemaid's Horror in spite of my repeated reminders that we nowadays have indoor plumbing, and would she please in the name of all that is fragrant use it? But hey.

For every up, at the Hope as elsewhere, there is a bit of a down. In July we observed half-visible in a cloud of butterflies – peacocks, red admirals, a gratifying slew of commas – a self-sown buddleia with flower spikes so black I thought they had contracted some frightful disease. When we picked some of this weird sport, though, it proved to be purple – a purple that makes 'Black Knight', otherwise known as Black Hole, look as brilliant as the sun at noon. The Advent darkness of the purple is relieved by brilliant little specks of orange at the centre of each floret, and close inspection is a great joy. The spike does have a more clotted aspect than your common or garden buddleia; and this density of floret may be the reason that when picked and brought indoors it is dead as mutton within the hour. Still, it is new, and the butterflies love it, so a bunch of cuttings are lined out in an inconspicuous corner. Fingers crossed, and cheerfulness prevails.

As far as garden visiting is concerned, this has been a year that has produced immense cheerfulness. It started with a visit to Tresco at the height of its May glory, echiums everywhere, geraniums dispensing the perfumes of Araby, trees sculptural and glorious, and blimey, the vistas. Tresco is very good at hijacking slices of land and seascape, and when there the Duchess becomes increasingly sullen, always a sign that she is deeply impressed.

After Tresco came Bryan's Ground, where the beautiful formalities on one side of the house are balanced by some genuine barminesses on the other side. These include a just about endless mown-grass avenue lined by yews growing from a waft of pignuts, a temple whose pillars are the trunks of wild cherry trees, and several splendid examples of landscape capture, in which the cunning Simon Dorrell has focused the attention of the stroller on his co-optings of significant hills and other intriguing chunks of the Marcher landscape, with or without ha-has. These vistas extend the garden, already pretty enormous, for several miles – though I am not entirely sure exactly how many, because the Duchess had started a train of reminiscence that made it impossible for anyone within half a mile to concentrate, and the only way out of it was to let her talk until she wound down.

The story, in case you were wondering, went like this. Her grandfather, a man of ambiguous tastes, had become irritated by the lack of interesting features in a minor vista from the east wing of the vast pile he inhabited in some county or other. He had therefore caused to be built on the summit of a distant hill a huge bronze sculpture of the Infant David in the worst possible Italian Gift Shop taste, and adding insult to injury had it gilded. The neighbours were appalled by the anatomical detailing of the thing, and the way it caught the low rays of the sun of an evening. The local cattle started to give sour milk, and a cloud of carrot fly and cabbage whites covered the *potagers* of the peasantry, and everyone knew what to blame. Luckily (said the Duchess) war broke out soon after this. And her grandmother, who of course was a friend of Hermann Goering, rang the Reichsmarschall in question and persuaded him to organise an air raid in the interest of pure aesthetics. So the Infant David was blown up, and the bronze fragments removed to be melted down for ships' propellers. And the grandfather, furiously indignant but unable in the prevailing austerity to replace the excrescence, made sure that poor Granny spent her war in Pentonville for consorting with the enemy, which of course was a great relief to us all. Where, said the Duchess, was I?

Landscape capture, I said. And before she could open her mouth I had bundled her on to the boat and sailed her up the west coast of Scotland, where the landscape does not so much capture gardens as kidnap them and chain them in place among the play of light and shade over the sea and the hills.

As usual, we dropped anchor off Li, the garden made by Hillary and Rick Rohde on the northern shore of the vast wilderness peninsula of Knoydart. Nowadays, this is a charming little house surrounded by a beautiful garden and an arboretum with vistas of the hills above Arnisdale and the rest of Loch Hourn, and the fearsome pyramid summit of Ladhar Bheinn. Rick found the place some thirty years ago as he was strolling hither and yon through the trackless wastes of the western Highlands. He fenced it against deer, planted trees, and for a while ran beef cattle, which in the autumn he drove to the roadhead at Arnisdale, two miles away across the loch but thirty miles away as the bullock ambles, with the assistance of his boots and a dog. Hillary, who coordinated the knitting efforts of the local crofters, pegged gently away at the garden, which to her surprise and nobody else's became a thing of astonishing beauty. Furthermore, it is unspoilt by coach tourists, because there is no road to it, and it is accessible only by sea; though it can be seen in glorious Technicolor in the book Hillary and Rick have put together.

The Duchess sat in Hillary's greenhouse looking at an extensive collection of rogersias. The place is supremely isolated, deeply eccentric, entirely beautiful and imbued with a massive common sense. I could see that she was going to have absolutely nothing to complain about, which is frustrating for her, and would be driving her in the direction of the Rohde gin supply, if there was one.

Then Hillary said, 'Shall we have some cake?'

The Duchess normally eschews cake, but Hillary is a specialist, and a thing slathered in cream and raspberries appeared. 'Goodness,' said the Duchess. And before I knew what was going on she had whipped out a chequebook and signed up for a copy of the Li volume, and as long as the bank honours a document lightly smeared with cake cream pinkened by contact with O My God It's the Fire Brigade lipstick by (possibly) Estée Lauder, the Rohdes have a sale on their hands.

After this we came home, and found yet more reasons to be cheerful in the kitchen garden. These included gallons of tomatoes, enormous sheaves of dahlias, and cucurbits to the point where in the small hours I wake up and hear with the ear of imagination the rumble of pumpkins trundling down the chute to the storage tables. Then the thought occurs that perhaps it is the Duchess, who has been reading the Li book, trying to jemmy open the gin cupboard to celebrate. I had better get up and have a look. But the nights are drawing in, and it is warm and cheerful in here, and can I be bothered?

Not really. Good night.

Nights in the Gardens of Spain

'IT's HERE,' said the Duchess, glaring out of the car window. 'I'm absolutely positive.'

But of course you do not know where here is, and given her past record for opinions unbased on anything but spleen you may be doubting the value of the Duchess's positiveness. Which makes two of us. I should therefore fill you in.

It was about midnight. We were somewhere in Spain, sitting in front of an enormous pair of wrought-iron gates set in a high wall that stretched infinitely to left and right, perhaps topped with broken glass; though the night, which was moonless and resembled a bag of black velvet, made it impossible to see what was on top of this wall, or even if it had a top. You would have needed a pogo stick to check, and neither I nor the Duchess does pogo sticks.

The Duchess was out of the car now, and I felt the old familiar gloom settle, for I knew the signs. She was on a mission. Sure enough, the yelling began. *¡Abre, abre!'* she cried, reinforcing her yells by running the ferrule of her umbrella across the ironwork, which was richly but fragilely gilded.

Someone appeared from the gate lodge. There was an exchange of remarks in Andaluz, which I construed as the minion demurring and the Duchess threatening dismissal. As so often, her commands were effective, and the portals swung wide, and I aimed the car up a drive while the Duchess sat beside me breathing damnation on all foreigners. On we drove, and on, and on between groves of holm oak and a small range of mountains and finally into a flat expanse on which formal gardens in the style of Villandry could be discerned. At the far side of all this lay the shadowy masses of an enormous house, with a tower at one end, a cupola in the middle, and somewhere over a few horizons of roofscape a bristle of pinnacles and *flèches* that implied a Gothic chapel, if not a full-scale convent. 'Dear little place,' said the Duchess fondly. 'It will be lovely to stay here again after all these years.'

It is never worth demurring in these situations. But what struck me like a big gloomy hammer was that in that whole gigantic edifice no light burned.

'We will go to the entrance front,' said the Duchess.

And thither we proceeded, weaving among courtyards and outcrops of masonry, and drew up at length under a *porte cochère*. I climbed out of the car and walked up the long flight of steps to the iron-studded double front door. I stood in front of it in the warm night, inhaling wafts of jasmine from patios invisible. Then I picked up the knocker and started walloping.

The sound boomed in vast interior spaces. The echoes faded. Silence fell. After what seemed like half an hour there was an odd rhythmic hissing, which resolved itself into the shuffle of feet on marble. A tiny wicket opened at head-height. 'Good evening,' I said, bursting into Spanish. 'I have brought the Duchess to see the Duchess of Alba, whose residence I believe this to be. She has been promised a cutting of the kapok tree, which she wishes to grow in the greenhouse at the Hope, though I must say that I feel the chances of it striking are somewhere between remote and non-existent.'

'*No está,*' said the door, emitting a cloud of sour wine and black tobacco.

'This is Spain!' cried the Duchess from the car. 'Tell the man to fetch a thumbscrew and put his hands out of that window thing!'

'*No está,*' said the door again. The wicket slammed shut, and I heard a creaking but agitated voice within yammering into a telephone. This was followed by the sound of distant sirens. It seemed to be the moment to leave.

Of the drive that followed I will only say that Spanish policemen, while diligent and even brave, do not have the background in garden design that enables one to make the best use of (say) the gravel paths of a formal garden, mazes planted along classical lines, and sudden ha-has. Nor, having failed to negotiate or indeed even locate such obstacles, do they have the energy to shut big wrought-iron gates after them. We therefore left several police cars inverted and smouldering in garden features and arrived unarrested in the city of Seville, where we caroused on the banks of the Guadalquivir and the Duchess gave some demonstrations of Flamenco dancing *à l'ancienne*.

This was in the month of September, and I was somewhat *distrait* at the thought of the pumpkins lying ripe among their fading vines in the kitchen garden at the Hope, and the daisies planted last year wasting their sweetness on what passes in Herefordshire for the desert air. The Duchess, however, was mad for kapok, having read goodness knows where that if you sleep with your head on a pillow stuffed with its fibres you would dream of home. Home, for the Duchess, means grandeur and the innocence of childhood, not (thanks to various horrid uncles and a very odd aunt) that she ever knew what that meant. After a few days of heat and tapas I suggested that we get on a flight, and as for the kapok, I had a pre-war lifejacket on which she could lay her head if she did not mind a slight smell of mould. Snorting, she dragged me out of the breakfast room and on to one of those open-topped buses.

In this revolting contraption we commenced a dismal progress round the boulevards, the Duchess glaring with fierce concentration at the passing scene, knuckles white on the safety rail. Suddenly she emitted a sharp cry, rushed down the stairs and hurled herself out of the double doors, deaf to the remonstrances of the bus pimp. Used to dealing with biddable Japanese and equally supine members in good standing of the National Trust, this grasping but weak functionary did not stand a chance. The sound of collisions and horns faded astern as we rushed into what turned out to be the Palacio de las Dueñas. 'Wha?' I said, or words to that effect.

'It is the city residence,' said the Duchess, 'of my dear old friend Alba, who was not at home the other night.'

And you could see why it would have been. Patio followed patio, enormous walls coated in jasmine and a sort of tweed of mixed bougainvilleas, beds full of clivias and roses. Huge Canary palms vaulted skywards, desperate to get their heads above the parapets. Plumbago was its usual quiet greyish-blue, but in such fearsome abundance that it was like being in a very discreet jungle. And in the furthest corner of the furthest patio, its fearsomely spiked and warted trunk rising from a pink scatter of its flowers, stood a kapok tree. 'Now,' said the Duchess. 'Where is my dear friend Alba?'

'Hard to say,' said a voice behind us. 'Seeing that she died in 2014.'

The Duchess whirled, and found herself looking at (I think) a gardener. I outlined our need for kapok material. 'Ah,' said the gardener. 'We use cuttings perhaps two metres long. Certainly I will send you some.'

The Duchess looked disappointed. She is only a Duchess because she married a Duke, poor man, and the Duchess of Alba was a Duchess in her own right, and it seems that there is a hierarchy even among Duchesses, and the Duchess is a fearsome snob. So I wrote our address on a piece of paper, and back to the Hope we came, which is all mists and mellow fruitfulness. If the cuttings ever arrive they will end up in the polytunnel, where they will die, or in the hall stand, where someone will use them as walking sticks. And the Duchess will carry on in the waking dream she calls life.

Just now, though, she is out after mushrooms, all of which she will fry in butter and eat herself. It is a splendid year for Death Caps, so I do hope she is lucky.

Market Forces

THE NEW WOOD AT THE HOPE is not as new as it was ten years ago. There are as yet no forest giants, but the trees are well away, and to walk through the thing is to get an insight into lostness unavailable on, say, a grass tennis court. The other day I was leading a party of weekend visitors through the thickest part of it when there was a splitting noise and down from the sky plummeted what looked like a dead Christmas tree. On closer inspection, this turned out to be the top third of a silver birch. Still closer inspection revealed that the reason for its descent lay with the fact that something had nibbled a ring all around the trunk, which had then rotted, and down it had come.

Someone suggested beavers, but of course this was nonsense, as beavers gnaw, not nibble, and besides, they are by no means arboreal. It was ruddy squirrels again. Instructing the staff to make tea for the visitors, I marched into the gunroom and leafed through the weaponry with a mounting sense of futility. Kill one squirrel and another five come along to take its place. By all accounts Hercules, during the decapitation phase of his *mano a mano* with the Lernaean Hydra, became somewhat depressed when the monster kept on growing new heads. I knew exactly how he felt. Seating myself on a wormy chair, I rested the chin on the fist and gave myself over to contemplation.

Guns, I reflected, were noisy, traps unfair, and poison ended up killing whatever eats squirrels. Then in a distant, ill-lit cellar of the mind something stirred: a half-memory of the Duchess speaking with uncharacteristic enthusiasm about a natural history item. The recollection was hazy, because obviously I had not really been listening. But the burden of it was that someone somewhere had discovered that pine martens eat squirrels like slugs eat lettuce, while red squirrels, selected by years of becoming martens' lunches, know how to stay out of their way. So all we had to do was start a marten farm.

Rapid telephoning ensued. English Nature, London Zoo and

several prominent furriers informed me that my chances of getting marten breeding stock were analogous to those of snowflakes in hell, and that I would just have to wait for the creatures to arrive as part of their natural spread. The closest marten I have seen to Herefordshire was waving its tail at me from a tree in the valley of the Munster Blackwater, so if it was going to get to the Hope by natural diffusion it was first going to have to learn to build a boat and navigate, and I did not have the requisite few million years in hand. So out I trudged into the fine drizzle that was falling, and gazed upon the little meadow the Duchess has forced us to fill with the bulbs of wild tulips and camassias and all that sort of thing. Waste of time, of course, because the voles get them. Still, we plant, and hope, and hope, and plant, and all flesh is as grass, and so on. By which you will be able to judge that the *cafard* was running strong, and existential despair had claimed me for its own.

Away I wandered until I found myself among a little cluster of bramble-clogged sheds that sits on the edge of the policies. Once they were kennels, and the niff of spaniels still lingers, and oddly enough I seemed to hear the sound of phantom barking. As I paused to disengage a bramble from the sweater, I realised I was wrong. This was nothing as melodious as a spaniel. It was the high, perfectly-bred quacking of a Duchess, punctuated by remarks from someone male whose voice had not yet broken, on the subject of ferrets. I paused behind a ruined wall, listening.

'When I was a gel,' said the Duchess, 'we used to have masses of ferrets. Well I say we, but of course it was the keepers. From time to time we used to steal them and put them in people's beds and they gave them the most awful bites. There was this film star who came to stay and woke up in the middle of the night with a pair of beady eyes glaring at her on the pillow by her head and she ran screaming out of the room claiming that they were her agent's. A drinker of course.'

'How interesting,' said the child, making a brave attempt to sound as if he meant it.

'It certainly is,' said the Duchess firmly. 'Cigarette?'

'I am trying to give them up,' said the voice, which I now

recognised as belonging to Evan, eleven, a tactful young relation.

'Helps with the smell,' said the Duchess, coughing.

'I think they smell jolly good,' said Evan. 'The ferrets, not the fags.'

The coughing stopped. 'Valuable expectorant,' wheezed the Duchess, and there was an edge to her voice that suggested it would soon be reinforced by the back of her hand.

This appendage is knuckledustered with dirty diamonds, and one did not want the poor boy to get blood poisoning. 'Ahem,' I therefore said, revealing myself. 'Lovely afternoon. Hello, Ev.'

Evan what-hoed, and we spoke of the weather, and I asked what was going on. 'The thing is,' said Evan, 'that the Duchess is buying ferret muck off me.'

'Muck?' I said. 'Ferret? Buying?'

'I sort of scrape it off the bottom of their cage,' said Evan.

Here the Duchess ground out her fag and began one of her monologues, taking as her text the article about pine martens to which   I alluded earlier. The voles, she pointed out, kept eating her tulip bulbs and camassias and what not (see above). The mustelid, by which she meant the family of animals that includes pine martens, polecats, ferrets, and otters, is the natural enemy of the vole as well as the grey squirrel. In the absence of pine martens or trained otters she had made Evan, a keen ferret-keeper, a proposition. Every time he cleaned out the ferret cage he would bring the result to the Hope, and she would give him two quid –

'Three,' said Evan.

– details, details, said the Duchess, but the point was that the ferret muck would be spread on the tulip/camassia/whatnot, hell, call it bulbs-in-grass bed, and the voles would flee, or anyway stay away.

'Three quid,' said Evan. The Duchess handed over the coins. Evan bit them and stowed them in his pocket, and we parted.

Three weeks later the world was perceptibly warmer, and the Duchess and I were eying the bulbs-in-grass bed, from which small green shoots were beginning to rise. At this moment Evan appeared, staggering under the weight of a reeking sack. 'More muck,' he said, as if we had no noses. 'Three quid please.'

The Duchess gave one of her least pleasant smiles, pointed out the green shoots, and told him to take his filthy muck away.

'But you promised,' said Evan. The Duchess mentioned her firmly-held belief that promises were made to be broken. Evan said, 'You sure?'

The Duchess said she was sure.

'Ferrets in the bed, dear mucky little guys,' said Evan with a meditative air. 'Quite a thought.'

The Duchess turned pale and gave it as her opinion that he was asking for a good spanking. Evan told her that this was illegal nowadays, and that what he was actually asking for was three quid as per contract.

'And how do you justify this?' said the Duchess.

'You get nice flowers in this grass and just you in your bed,' said Evan. 'I get three quid. Market forces.'

The Duchess scowled, of course, and I saw with joy that she had been outsmarted by this brilliant young entrepreneur. She handed over the funds, and Evan went on his way rejoicing. Next time I saw him I gave him a fiver as a bonus. The bulbs are lovely, the tulips like jewels against the velvet-green grass.

But that is scarcely the point.

The Orange Blossom Special

IT WAS THE FAG END OF WINTER, and darkness lay on the face of the waters. I was gazing out of the morning-room window, weighing in the mind the respective advantages of planting water-lilies or rice, when a canoe glided over the brown flood formerly known as the Big Lawn. The Duchess was at the helm, plying the paddle with casual expertise. The diamonds on her fingers glinted in a fugitive gleam of sun, or perhaps it was an eel.

Normally in these situations she drifts idly hither and yon, re-flecting on the injustices handed out by a hostile universe, and can be left to her own devices for weeks at a time. This morning, how-ever, there was something unnervingly purposeful about her. She paddled towards the house with a fierce j-stroke, cutting a slice out of the flood until she was brought to an abrupt halt by some-thing hard just below the surface. I saw instantly that he had gone aground on the upper slopes of the Giant's Keyring, one of the abstract sculptures that contributes so much to the *feng shui* of the Hope. The impact tipped her into the water, where she floundered, cursing, until I rowed out to fetch her in the pram dinghy in those watery times permanently moored to the bootscraper by the back door.

By the time I got her into the house she was blue (cold, not blood) and roaring between chattering teeth for hot toddy. Giving her this would of course have precipitated weeks of blackouts, vandalism and sea shanties sung at inopportune moments. She was therefore filled with tea, which she hates, and despatched to a warm room in the Tower, where a retainer was detailed to massage her violently wearing sacking gloves. Judging by the yells that floated down the stone stairs she soon seemed to be warming up nicely. I sat by the fire, toying with a seed catalogue and reflecting nervously on the Wrath to Come. Sure enough, it came.

The less said about it the better, really, except that I found my-self swallowing the key of the drinks cupboard while she patted me down for the packet of Capstan Full Strength she maintained I must be hiding in a pocket somewhere. The only way I could distract her from nipping off to the toolshed for a felling axe was to engage her in conversation about Foreign Parts, preferably warm and dry. This had the desired effect. She bid Bahamas, because poor darling Edward the Eighth always said it was so lovely, and I bid Dogsleds in Norway, just because, and she bid Bermuda, and I bid the Azores, and in the end we compromised on southwest Spain, though after we had duly signed the agreement I realised with some nervousness that it is the home of sherry. Off (the waters showing no sign of receding, and the floods becoming skimmed with ice) we went.

This sounds as if we were in perfect agreement: not, sadly, the case. On the journey to Spain, conducted via various trains, she showed a disturbing tendency to vanish. She had to be retrieved from the lost property office at the Gare de Lyon, the central police station in Barcelona, and a flat in Cordoba into which she had moved at the invitation of a gypsy guitarist – a talented player in the flamenco idiom who shared what was effectively a bedsit with several goats, a flock of chickens and twelve of his cousins. Run to earth, she seemed almost relieved, and came quietly, as if penitent, or more likely reculing pour mieux sauter.

We drove in a hire car down the long sandy road into the flatlands of the Guadalquivir delta. Hundreds of square miles of it are covered with polytunnels, which supply Europe with most of its strawberries. The Duchess began to look smug; she will only eat strawberries she has picked herself, in the month of June, and after a whiff of the chemicals emanating from the tunnels my sympathy with her view, already strong, intensified. The tunnels gave way after a few hours to forests of umbrella pines, which had replaced the native cork oaks felled for firewood by the freezing peasantry during the incompetent austerities of the Franco regime. Finally, we arrived in the village of El Rocio.

El Rocio has hitching posts for horses instead of car parking spaces, and looks like a set for a Western. (This is the wrong way round. Columbus came here to get his horses before discovering America, and on arrival copied the local architecture; so actually all Western movie sets look like El Rocio). The Duchess was largely brought up by horses, so she found herself perfectly at home, and seemed relieved that nothing resembling a garden could survive in the sandy soil of the place. She was, however, thrilled to find two hundred square miles of national park right on the doorstep, and even more so when she discovered that no human beings were allowed into it, except with guides. So in we drove, admiring a splendid landscape of cork oaks over which Imperial eagles soared. The Duchess was so overcome by the sight of her first lynx that she rushed out of the Land Rover and followed the creature into a lentisk bush. Finishing the retying of an errant shoelace, I remarked in a Spanish carefully stripped of enthusiasm that it was possible that she would be eaten. Our guide told me that in fact the lynxes only ate rabbits, and that went for the eagles too. Unaccountably depressed, I marched into the lentisk bush, which like all lentisk bushes is hollow in the middle, hauled forth the Duchess, by now smelling powerfully of tomcats, and carted her off to Cadiz.

Here we strolled the seafront of the ancient city, pausing by a pair of enormous multi-trunked aerial-rooted trees covering between them the best part of an acre of a park. The Duchess unhesitatingly identified them as baobabs. Nodding and smiling commenced, though they were of course *Ficus macrophylla*, nothing to do with baobabs, and shining examples of what your ordinary accountant's-office rubber plant can achieve if let rip for a couple of hundred years in a beneficial climate. Before a botanical argument could develop we decamped to Jerez to buy a hat in the splendid shop of Antonio Garcia. After a light lunch of octopus and anchovies, we strolled by the Alcazar, where the smell of orange blossom came in mighty wafts, and lesser kestrels hawked among the pigeons. When I turned to mention the beauties of the scene to the Duchess, I was surprised to find her no longer at my side. The surprise did not, however, last. The sound of distant singing came floating through the ether from the nearby Tio Pepe bodega: *Donkey Riding*, it was, one of her favourite shanties in the bad old days. Sure enough, there in a cellarful of barrels was the Duchess, standing on a hogshead, a bottle in each hand, singing her black heart out to a group of tourists from Milwaukee.

By the time I had disentangled the situation and dispensed a few fifty-euro notes she had reached the penitent-and-headachy stage. Following her binding over to keep the peace by the Guardia Civil she moved about her avocations with a pensive air, sniffing the jasmine with which the town was festooned and audibly making resolutions about leading a Better Life. People are saying she has changed. Those who know her well, however, conclude that she is merely scheming something.

Still, summer is icumen in, and the trunks of the trees in the Hope woods are spiky with swags of roses, like the pillars of a ruined green temple. The sky is the colour of a ripe peach, a small fierce sun is sinking something north of west, and the click of croquet balls is heard from the Little Lawn. We are using the pram dinghy, inverted, to force cardoons, and the Duchess is still keeping quiet. Nothing lasts for ever, though. In an uncertain world you can be certain of that.